MEDICAL SOCIOLOGY

and

CULTURAL ANTHROPOLOGY

of

SPORT and PHYSICAL EDUCATION

Publication Number 569
AMERICAN LECTURE SERIES®

A Monograph in
The BANNERSTONE DIVISION *of*
AMERICAN LECTURES IN SPORTSMEDICINE

Edited by
ERNST JOKL, M.D.
University of Kentucky
Lexington, Kentucky

MEDICAL SOCIOLOGY

and

CULTURAL ANTHROPOLOGY

of

SPORT AND PHYSICAL EDUCATION

By

ERNST JOKL, M.D.

University of Kentucky
Lexington, Kentucky

CHARLES C THOMAS • PUBLISHER
Springfield • Illinois • U.S.A.

Published and Distributed Throughout the World by

CHARLES C THOMAS • PUBLISHER

BANNERSTONE HOUSE

301-327 East Lawrence Avenue, Springfield, Illinois, U.S.A.

NATCHEZ PLANTATION HOUSE

735 North Atlantic Boulevard, Fort Lauderdale, Florida, U.S.A.

With THOMAS BOOKS careful attention is given to all details of manufacturing and design. It is the Publisher's desire to present books that are satisfactory as to their physical qualities and artistic possibilities and appropriate for their particular use. THOMAS BOOKS will be true to those laws of quality that assure a good name and good will.

Printed in the United States of America

Q-1

INTRODUCTION

T HIS BOOK consists of three essays. The first, entitled "Sport and Culture" was prepared for presentation at the Second Plenary Session of the Unesco Conference on "The Cultural Value of Sport in the Orient and the Occident," scheduled for December 1962 in Manila. The second deals with a study of data collected during the 1952 Olympic Games in Helsinki, undertaken jointly with my friends and colleagues M. J. Karvonen, J. Kihlberg, A. Koskela and L. Noro of the Finnish Institute of Occupational Health. Its concept as well as methodology will, it is believed, be applied in future researches of a similar kind. The third essay, "Sport and Human Development" has appeared in Unesco's *International Journal of Adult and Youth Education* (1962, IV). It forms part of a review undertaken together with Mr. Rene Maheu to whose article I have referred in chapter I, and the Right Hon. Philip Noel Baker.

E. J.

CONTENTS

Contents

MEDICAL SOCIOLOGY

and

CULTURAL ANTHROPOLOGY

of

SPORT and PHYSICAL EDUCATION

SPORT AND CULTURE

ALLEGORICAL CONNOTATIONS OF "WORK" AND "REST"

T HE biblical story of the expulsion of Adam and Eve from Paradise conveys the divine injunction that "mankind is to earn its bread by the sweat of its brow." Work, we are told, was to be punishment for man's transgression of the law. Contrariwise, rest was considered a reward. God himself rested after He had created the world: and He sanctified the Sabbath.

While to the scientific inquirer exercise and recovery are ubiquitous physiological events, the terms work and rest have assumed anthropological connotations of their own: the one carries a curse, the other a blessing.

Though the acceptance of the working day has marked the beginning of all civilization, it was left to Western society to declare work a virtue. "Ora et labora" has been a leitmotiv of the Catholic Church during one of its most dynamic periods. Leopold von Ranke, the historian, once remarked that the conversion of the Germans to Christianity in the 8th century led to their habit of rising early in the morning to attend mass instead of sleeping until noon as had been their custom before. It was also thus that they got used to regular labor.

WORK AS SLAVERY

Whatever virtue may be attached to work in its various forms, to many it remained a curse. It is little more than a hundred years ago that the abolition of child labor in England initiated one of the greatest social revolutions in the history of mankind, a revolution which brought to an end an epoch in which work had all too often been identical with slavery. The following excerpts from the evidence given before the Committee on Factory Chil-

3

Fig. 1.

Fig. 2.

Figs. 1 and 2. Taken from the Children's Employment Commission Report of 1842. Figure 1 shows children dragging a coal truck; Figure 2 shows children being lowered into a mine shaft.

With the invention of machinery, a horde of workless, starving vagrants had flocked from the countryside into the towns. Children were driven by the poverty of their parents into factories and mines. Child-slaves, orphaned and friendless, were supplied in droves by the workhouses to employers. Children of ten, of seven, five and even of three spent twelve hours at a

dren's Labor in 1831 in England affords a glimpse into a world that—one is happy to say—has now virtually disappeared.

> Question: At what time in the morning, in the brisk time, did these girls go to the mills?
>
> Answer: In the brisk time, for about six weeks, they have gone at 3 o'clock in the morning, and ended at 10, or nearly half past, at night.
>
> Q: What intervals were allowed for rest or refreshment during those nineteen hours of work?
>
> A: Breakfast, a quarter of an hour, and dinner half an hour, and drinking a quarter of an hour.
>
> Q: Was any of that time taken up in cleaning the machinery?
>
> A: They generally had to do what they call dry down: sometimes this took the whole of the time at breakfast or drinking; and they were to get their breakfast and dinner as they could; if not, it was brought home.
>
> Q: Had you not great difficulty in awakening your children to this excessive labor?
>
> A: Yes, in the early time we had to take them up asleep and shake them, when we got them on the floor to dress them, before we could get them off to their work; but not so in the common hours . . .
>
> Q: What was the length of time they could be in bed during those long hours?
>
> A: It was near 11 o'clock before we could get them into bed after getting a little victuals, and then at morn-

---

time in the darkness of the mines. Lord Shaftesbury was among the most active proponents of reforms. "Never," he said in a parliamentary debate on child labor in the House of Commons, "have I seen such a display of selfishness, frigidity to every human sentiment, such ready and happy self-delusion." In 1850, children of less than ten as well as girls and women were excluded altogether from the mines. But it was not until 1875 that boy chimney sweepers were prohibited. The seventies saw compulsory free education established throughout Great Britain and thus a barrier was interposed between children and the factories. In the same decade the first kindergartens were introduced. The Society for the Prevention of Cruelty to Children, founded in 1872, took the initiative in promulgating progressive social legislation. (cp. Sylvia Lynd.: *English Children*. London, William Collins, 1942.)

ing my mistress used to stay up all night, for fear
that we could not get them ready for the time; sometimes we have gone to bed, and one of us generally
awoke.

Q: At what time did you get them up in the morning?
A: In general me and my mistress got up at 2 o'clock
to dress them.

Q: So that they had not above four hours' sleep at this
time? The common hours of labor were from 6 in
the morning till half past eight at night?

A: Yes.

Q: With the same intervals for food?

A: Just the same.

Q: Were the children excessively fatigued by this labor?

A: Many time; we have cried often when we have given
them the little victualling we had to give them; we
had to shake them, and they have fallen to sleep with
the victuals in their mouths many a time.

To understand why, during the past decades, sport has become
one of the major leisure pursuits of mankind, it must be realized
that the concepts of both leisure and sport have only recently
assumed their present meaning. The idea that time for leisure
would be available to the common man sounded revolutionary not
so long ago when the worker unless he was working, rested to
recuperate from and gather new strength for work. The boys
and girls who slaved in coal mines and textile mills around the
middle of the nineteenth century had neither the time nor the
strength to play. Their as well as their elders' situation was in-
comparably worse than that which had prevailed during the
preceding millenium in the relatively stable, predominantly rural
village environment throughout Western Europe.

VEBLEN AND RUSSELL ON LEISURE

In 1899, Thorstein Veblen, the American sociologist, published
a book *The Theory of the Leisure Class* in which he argued that
from primitive times to modern days most societies have supported a leisure class. Veblen defined leisure as the "non-produc-
tive consumption of time," and leisure people as "propertied non-
industrial consumers." These people were not lazy or unem-

Fig. 3. One of the noteworthy achievements of mission work in Africa was the introduction of young boys and girls from primitive societies into dignified, meaningful and economically valuable forms of vocational work. Scenes like the one above which I saw during a visit to an Anglican Mission Station in the Transkei in Southern Africa, convey a distinctly pleasant and esthetically satisfactory impression. Labor such as the spinning of wool which the girls are being taught has a purpose; it is unfragmented and the success or failure of the workers' effort is readily recognizable.

ployed. On the contrary, they were usually in government, war, sport or devout observances. They lived upon the productive work of others and signified their position in society by their "conspicuous wealth" and their "conspicuous consumption," phrases which have won their place in economic and social literature. In the United States of America, Veblen detected his leisure class chiefly in the Southern States where slavery existed until the Civil War and where a planter aristocracy lived a fairly leisured existence based upon slave and later cheap labor.

Thirty years ago, the case for leisure for the common man was summarized by Bertrand Russell in an essay entitled "In Praise of Idleness." Russell asserted that there is far too much work done in the world, that immense harm is caused by the belief that work is virtuous, and that what needs to be preached in modern in- dustrial countries is quite different from what had always been preached. From the beginning of civilization until the Industrial Revolution, he said, a man could as a rule produce by hard work little more than was required for the subsistence of himself and his family, although his wife worked at least as hard as he did, and his children added their labor as soon as they were old enough to do so. Modern technique, he foresaw, would make an end to a time in which leisure was the prerogative of a small privi- leged class. Leisure would become a right evenly distributed throughout the community. The morality of work, he wrote, is the morality of slaves, and the modern world has no need for slavery. Athenian slave owners, he pointed out, employed part of their leisure in making a permanent contribution to civilization which would have been impossible under just economic systems. Leisure is essential to civilization and in former times leisure for the few was only rendered possible by the labors of the many. But their labors were valuable, not because work is good, but because leisure is good.

In America, Russell observed, men often work long hours even when they are already well off; in fact, some of them dislike leisure not only for themselves but also for their sons. Oddly enough, they do not mind their wives and daughters having no work at all. The snobbish admiration of uselessness which in an aristocratic society once extended to both sexes is under a plutocracy confined to women; this, however, does not make it more in agreement with common sense.

The wise use of leisure is a product of civilization and education. A man who has worked long hours all his life is likely to feel bored if he suddenly becomes idle. But without a considerable amount of leisure a man is cut off from many of the best things. For thousands of years, the rich have preached the dignity of labor while taking care themselves to remain undignified in this respect. The notion that the desirable activities are only those that bring a profit has made everything topsy-turvy. We think too much of production and too little of consumption.

Russell recommended that education should provide tastes which would enable a man to use leisure intelligently. In the past there was a small leisure class and a large working class. The leisure class enjoyed advantages for which there was no basis in social justice though it invented theories to justify these privileges. However, it did contribute nearly the whole of what we call civilization. It cultivated the arts and discovered the sciences; it wrote the books, invented the philosophies and refined social relations.* Even the liberation of the oppressed has frequently been inaugurated from above. Without the leisure class mankind would never have emerged from barbarism.

It is of great interest to note that as late as the early thirties Russell did not refer to the sportsmovement as an activity that did or would play a part in the leisure pursuits of the masses. Actually, none of the sociologists born during the Victorian period foresaw this development. Russell's prediction that leisure would cause the masses to acquaint themselves with philosophy, the arts and literature, has certainly not become true. Nor has George Bernard Shaw been right in saying that art would refine the people's

> "sense of character and conduct, of justice and sympathy, their self-knowledge, self-control, precision of action and considerateness, and make them intolerant of baseness, cruelty, injustice and intellectual superficiality or vulgarity."

---

* Professor Ely Devons of the London School of Economics, said in 1963 that the chief tasks of English universities today is that of making provision for an "intellectual leisured class" (*Listener*, March 14, 1963).

DISCREPANCY BETWEEN SOCIAL AND CULTURAL
ROLE OF SPORT

Maheu who considers sport and physical education training "human diciplines with a social function and a role in the formation and full development of the personality," has pointed out that the roots of sport and culture are identical in that both spring from leisure, from the availability of spare time and unspent energy. However, if we take culture in the sense of any of its current forms of expression, there are today no demonstrable contacts between it and sport. Though the modern sports movement has gained widespread *social* acceptance, there have been hardly any worthwhile *cultural* works with sport as their basis. In philosophy, literature, the theater, even the cinema, in painting, sculpture and music there are no artistic counterpoints to the struggles and dramas of athletics; no symphonies, songs and ballets, no preludes or meditations that reflect or deepen the concept of the balanced mastery of body and soul, which, we are sure, sport is able to establish. Contests in literature, music and sculpture which Coubertin wanted to be integrated with the Olympic Games have yielded lamentably mediocre results and they were dropped from the program since 1956. All this adds up to the "astounding, dismaying, infuriating and even, to be frank, scandalous situation in which sport, otherwise triumphant, is excluded from what I shall not call culture but culture's modes of expression."

THE CONCEPT OF CULTURE

Sigmund Freud wrote in 1902 that all culture, all civilization is based on the repression of natural instincts; that mankind achieves culture only by pushing under its strongest emotional drives; and that this repression breeds tension which in turn leads to outbursts of violence, war and crime. Other possibilities of canalizing these tensions did not occur to him so as they did not occur to Russell with his exaggerated belief in the "intelligence of the masses." In any event, neither of these two great thinkers took cognizance of the sports and physical education movement which began to grow up during their lifetime.

The German word "Kultur" which Freud used is not synonymous with either of the two English terms "culture" and "civilization." Actually, the English term "culture" has two different connotations. Anthropologists and sociologists apply it to describe a type of society identifiable by its technical, religious, moral, economic, social and artistic pecularities. Thus, we speak of Polynesian, South American or Scandinavian cultures. But the word "culture" has also a second sense—the sense in which one speaks of a "cultured person," or a Minister of Culture, or a cultural counsellor at an embassy; of someone cultivated in literature, art, languages, history and so forth; and of course manners; a sense which is allied to the concept of excellence. It was of this last sense of culture that a hundred years ago Matthew Arnold was thinking when he defined culture as "acquainting ourselves with the best that has been said and done in the world."*

Sir Charles Snow has said that what previously was looked upon as "culture" has now become "two cultures"; one which is scientifically orientated; while the other complies with the criteria of humanistic tradition. However, Lord Hailsham, Minister of Science in England, has recently emphasized that it is impossible to draw a line between "the sciences" and "the humanities." "My Department," he explained, "had to discuss the question whether anthropology was a science, and we were told by the Treasury that physical anthropology was a science and social anthropology was an art." Dr. Magnus Pyke, looking from a different angle upon the same problem arrived at the following conclusion: "If we wish to reflect upon the relationship between a man and a woman, we can turn for enlightenment either to Romeo and Juliet of the humanists or to the Kinsey Report of Science."†

MAHEU ON NATURE OF SPORT IN TECHNOLOGICAL SOCIETIES

According to Maheu, in most societies in which the modern sports movement has taken roots, "culture" has remained a pre-

---

* As to his own compatriots, Arnold saw them divided into three kinds: the upper classes "with their blood sports and drink and playing cards" whom he called "barbarians"; the middle class "caring for nothing but moral rectitude and money" who were to him "Philistines"; and the "populace" which was "brutalized by illiteracy and poverty."

† cp. also editorial article in *Journal of the American Medical Association* of April 13, 1963, "The 'Art' and 'Science' of Medicine."

rogative of a minority. The bulk of sport supporters do not belong to this minority. "It is one of the major aberrations of our
culture," he writes, "that many forms in which it expresses itself
lie beyond the reach of the workers and the peasants." Sport on
the other hand has attained its firmest grip upon the classes which
are—or were—the least privileged. Sport thus represents a form
of social elevation as well as an advance towards a status of
greater equality and freedom. This is one of the reasons why
sport has become a mass movement; but also why sport has so far
remained separate from culture pursuits. The categorical significance of the newly emerging *science and philosophy of sport* lies
in the fact that it represents a new effort of bridging the gap
between intellectualism and those areas of life which are shared
by all. The science of sport is derived from lived as well as
reflected human existence.

It is too early to assess the influence which this new development will exert upon society. Current humanistic theory does not
yet admit that the body may be of equal dignity with the heart,
the mind and the soul. Contemporary thinking is still permeated
by philosophical teachings to the effect that the body represents
the animal part of man which must be kept under. In our civilization the body ranks low in the scale of values. In Western
societies the body has for centuries been assailed on two fronts:
it was anathematized as sinful and it was made a target for contempt. Religious ethics, contemporary literature, the utilitarian
ideology of mechanization and absolute scientific positivism, all
have the disparagement of the body in common. Maheu stresses
the contrast between the respect for the body which prevailed
in antiquity and to a lesser extent still prevailed in the Renais-
sance, with the contempt for the body which characterizes the
intellectual climate in our time.

In current literature, the body, if treated at all, is considered
synonymous with sex. But of all bodily manifestations, sex is of
least relevance to the physical phenomena with which sport is
concerned; while those bodily manifestations of sport to which
specific human significance attaches are looked upon by scientists as if they were equivalents of the kinetic performances of
machines. Such an attitude is all the more anachronous since

machines tend to render the body useless, turn it into an automaton.

> "Machines are taking over more and more what the body used to do and science, that essential and determining factor in modern civilization, is perhaps the most deadly enemy of any humanism of the body; for in the final count the whole teaching of science is that the body is merely a machine and can be improved by means which practically deny its humanity."
>
> (Maheu)

With the advent of the industrial age the sociological status of the "populace" has undergone a change. Illiteracy and extreme poverty have virtually gone; child labor has gone. In terms of social justice a lot has been gained, though at a cost that was altogether unforeseen. Freud's view was vindicated as those of us who have witnessed events in Europe between 1933 and 1945 know only too well. The new status of the "masses," characterized by the mechanization of transport, by the emergence of a white collar class of workers, by the bureaucratization of life and by the automatization of production has repressed natural instincts to an extent that is without parallel in the history of mankind.

Homo faber had become homo sedentarius. However, the ancient curse allegedly imposed upon work seems to have remained in force, even though the biblical injunction that mankind is to earn its bread by the sweat of its brow no longer applies in industrial societies. The physical stress of labor has been largely eliminated by the introduction of machines. As a result of this development, man's "sense of movement" and with it its natural relationship to his body have deteriorated. Fundamental instincts and emotional outlets which physical exercise in its various forms had afforded in the past are no longer available. In 1961, two American physicians, H. Kraus and W. Raab wrote a book entitled *Hypokinetic Disease* in which a new category of health hazards is described, hazards due to the lack of exercise in our technological world.

THE CONTEMPORARY SCENE IN THE UNITED STATES

Because of the magnitude of the problem, President Eisenhower and President Kennedy have made public statements on the need to adopt measures to counteract the increasing trend toward unfitness in the United States. Evidently, universal affluence is not an unmixed blessing. The great potentialities of sport and physical education as re-integrating influences upon life have so far not been fully utilized. A recent American survey assessed the leisure activities of people over 15 years of age on a given weekday: 57% watched television, 38% visited with friends or relatives, 33% worked around the yard or garden, 27% perused newspapers, 18% read books, 17% went for pleasure driving, 14% listened to records, 11% attended meetings or other organizational activities, 10% were engaged in special hobbies like woodworking or knitting; and 8% had gone out for dinner. Sport was not among the ten most frequent leisure activities. The U.S. Opinion Research Corporation Study in which information was obtained from a national probability sample of 5,021 persons, revealed that in the age group 15-19 not more than one quarter had indulged in sport on a given day.

In a recent American book on *Time, Work and Leisure** it was stated that two-thirds of college educated women over 18 years of age and more than four-fifths of women who never attended college were engaged in no sport whatsoever. Of the minority who did participate in sport, as few as 13.5% and 6.4%, respectively, included swimming in their activity schedule. Only about 10% of women practiced systematically golf, tennis, bowling, basketball, softball, volleyball; while even fewer indulged regularly in ice skating, skiing, toboganing in winter and fishing and boating in the summer.

Though the number of people who watch sporting events is much greater than that of those who participate, the amount of money spent in the United States for television repairs alone is much greater than that spent on all spectator sports, including baseball, basketball and football.

To place all these facts into perspective, it is also necessary to remember that the United States produces many of the world's best performers in several of the chief branches of athletics. Because of the favorable nutritional, health and other environmental conditions which characterize the economic status of the people in

---

* Sebastian de Grazia, Twentieth Century Fund, New York, 1962.

the United States as well as in all other technologically advanced countries, their potential physical performance capacity has greatly benefited. This is shown by the acceleration of their growth during the past hundred years. However, the transformation of performance-potential into performance presupposes sustained application, effort and continuous training.

PLESSNER ON FRAGMENTATION OF LABOR

Helmut Plessner has pointed out that the traditional pilgrimage to Mecca which until not so long ago necessitated several weeks of walking, can now be undertaken by plane within hours or minutes. The result is that "the pilgrim arrives at the Holy Shrine in advance of his mind." Similarly, modern labor no longer conveys the sense of satisfaction that once came with the completion of a meaningful task. Work on assembly lines in factories is repetitive, senseless and boring. The occupational situation of the majority of white collar workers is frustrating. The worker as a human being has become anonymous. Fragmentation of labor and depersonalization of the laborer engender powerful inner tensions.

There is another aspect to consider: the general lack of recognizability of success and achievement of the individual worker. The progressive specialization of the production process presupposes acquaintance with the specific nature of the occupational activities that are demanded, an acquaintance which nobody is able to obtain in fields of employment other than his own. We know little of what the next person is doing, how well he is accomplishing his task and how successful he is in his career. Then there is the fact that the industrial world depends upon science. Not only the learned professions but at an ever growing rate also the crafts and other vocations now demand highly differentiated, intellectualized and organized preparation, often over many years.

Sport is capable of establishing a new balance vis-a-vis the inequalities that are thus caused by the steadily progressing transformation of society. Sport renders possible the expression and the satisfaction of many desires which the modern world awakens as well as represses; desires for recreation and social contact, for aggression and play, for self-assuredness and hero worship. True, athletics and sport are not the only means to attain such satisfaction; but they would seem to be among the most readily accessible and the most rewarding.* The universal recognizability of success and failure in sport is an essential element of communication and thus a means of advancement of freedom. Outside of sport, the range within which workers can move about without restraint and project their personality has become steadily decreasing with the uniformization of their environment. The trend towards restriction of freedom of self-projection has progressed pari passu with all recent material achievements. Press, radio, television, movies, organized traveling and mass

---

* Albert Camus said of his student days: "Sport was the main occupation of all of us, and continued to be mine for a long time. That is where I had my only lessons in ethics . . ." In his novel "La Chute," the main character of the story faithfully reflects the writer's personal attitude when he says: "I was really sincere and enthusiastic during the period when I played games, and also in the army when I acted in plays which we put on for enjoyment . . . Even today, the stadium crammed full of spectators for a Sunday match, and the theater which I loved with unequalled intensity, are the only places in the world where I feel innocent." (cp. John Cruickshank.: Albert Camus and the Literature of Revolt. Oxford University Press, 1959.)

"With my eldest son, who is 11, I go to a track at the foot of Parliament Hill in London on most Sunday mornings. We both belong to a North London athletics club. We find ourselves changing in a room which frequently contains a mixture of schoolboys, undergraduates, building labourers, clerks, teachers and lawyers ranging in age from 10 to 75. I am glad this is so, though I would not be stupid enough to say that all the uneasy suspicions between men of different generations and classes are thereby removed.

Social communication is made easier, and not only with others—between myself and my son too. Through doing althletics together, my son has a kind of induction to manhood and I a kind of fulfillment of fatherhood. I have a second chance of realizing, through him, some failed ambitions, and I can experience the joy of fashioning him, if only to a slight extent, in my own image. This is one of the meanings, or needs of parenthood. Together we can grow up and maintain our affection through a common enterprise. We do not need to talk or to be self-consciously father and son. We get up early on a summer morning, run over Hampstead Heath and through Ken Wood. We learn the rudimentary art of running, hurdling and throwing the javelin. We can feel cool air on our cheeks, sustain our limbs in a rhythm of effort, and later feel the glow of a really deserved relaxation. I realize there will be a time when we shall not want to do this, but for the moment it is a breathtaking projection of idealism—of the individual who is utterly dependent on his own fragile resources but also inescapably linked by invisible threads to his own flesh and blood and hence to mankind." (Peter Townsend, The Man Inside: Idealism and Athletics, *The Listener*, London, June 27, 1963.) (cp. also p. 90.)

fabrication of goods reduce the scope of private existence to a minimum. In this calamitous situation sport offers possibilities for display of the self which life otherwise does not render feasible. This statement applies chiefly to the active participants in athletics, but within limits also to the much greater numbers of spectators who identify themselves with the spectacle that takes place before their eyes.

EMPATHY AND CATHARSIS

Like the art connoisseur, Maheu says, the spectator at a sporting contest is linked with the object of the event by a "current of sympathetic participation." In the theater as well as in the stadium an intense empathy develops between spectator and performer. "Spectator sports," Maheu writes, "are the true theater of our day." Sport, because it involves a particular facet of contest-play, is able to release and, in the Aristotelian sense, to purge the emotions of the spectator just as effectively as any work of art in general and the theater in particular. In reference to this close link generating a current of understanding and support from nameless crowds of watchers and listeners to the individual taking the sporting stage and "expanding himself," Maheu says that it takes us back to the very start of the theater of antiquity, the theater of Greece. Like culture and the arts in general, sport exteriorizes the feelings and emotions of the player, and by empathy causes the spectator to experience "catharsis," the purification of the soul of which Aristotle has written long ago.

Lewis Mumford has pointed out that sport presents three main elements: the spectacle, the competition, and the personalities of the gladiators. The spectacle itself introduces the esthetic element, so often lacking in the "paleotechnic industrial environment" itself. The race is run or the game is played within a frame of spectators, tightly massed: the movements of this mass, their cries, their songs, their cheers, are a constant accompaniment of the spectacle: they play, in effect, the part of the Greek chorus in the new machine-drama, announcing what is about to occur and underlining the events of the contest. Through his place in the chorus, the spectator finds special release: he is now at one with a primitive undifferentiated group . . . feels relieved from

Fig. 4. Pieter Bruegel (1525-1569), Peasant Dance (Kunsthistorisches Museum, Vienna) (44⅞ x 64⅜), one of the greatest paintings of the Flemish master, attains its artistic objectives by the concentrated representation of individual and group action which conveys the spontaneous enjoyment that comes from the "dissolution of space," engendered by the combination of music and movement of the kind that are involved in dancing. In a unique manner, the picture appeals to the senses of the onlooker who realizes the objective of the artist.

the passive role of taking orders and automatically filling them, of conforming by means of a reduced "I" to a magnified "it." In the sports arena the sports spectator has the illusion of being completely mobilized and utilized. Moreover, the spectacle itself is one of the richest satisfactions for the esthetic sense that the machine civilization offers to those that have no key to any other form of culture: the spectator knows the style of his favorite contestant in the way that the painter knows the characteristic line or palette of his master and he reacts to the bowler, the pitcher,

Fig. 5. Jan Steen's (1626-1679) painting, The Skittle Players (13 x 10½, National Gallery, London), completed in 1652, is one of a series of pictures which the artist depicts the manners and morals of the peasantry of the time, their way of life and all the gaiety and drollery that went with it. "The ideal moment," Hegel wrote over a century ago, "consists precisely in this carefree license. This is the Sunday of life, levelling all before it and doing away with what is evil. Men endowed with so much good humor cannot be mean and vile at heart."

Fig. 6. Gustave Courbet's (1819-1877) Les Demoiselles au Bord de la Seine (left), (Petit Palais, Paris 173 x 205 cm) and Pablo Picasso's (born 1881) Les Demoiselles au Board de la Seine after Courbet (right), (Offentliche Kunstsammlung, Basel, 100 x 200 cm). The latter was painted as a replica of Courbet's work in a deliberately fragmented technique which Picasso cultivated between 1945 and 1950. It allegorizes a trend which pervaded and continues to pervade contemporary civilization. Though esthetically marking a decline of standards that seemed to be firmly established during the preceding centuries, the artistic significance of Picasso's work lies in the fact that it expresses intelligently and sensitively a development which for better or for worse characterizes the social climate of his time.

the punter, the server, the air ace, with a view, not only to his success in scoring but to the esthetic spectacle itself. This point has been stressed in bull-fighting; but of course it applies to every form of sport.

CHANGING LEISURE PATTERNS REFLECTED IN ART

The profound changes which the Industrial Revolution has introduced into the leisure pattern of society are reflected in the artistic styles, techniques, subjects and interpretations of the past 4 or 5 centuries. Pieter Bruegel's "Peasant Dance" which takes us back to the attractive village life of the Flemish people in the 16th century, radiates a human warmth and wholesomeness much of which has since been lost. Jan Steen's picture of "The Skittle Players" similarly mirrors the relaxed informality of rural recreation around 1650. Gustave Courbet's portrait "Les demoiselles au bord de la Seine," painted in 1856, still emanates the quiet and idyllical spirit of leisure at its best. Less than a century later, artists began to give us images of a different world. The

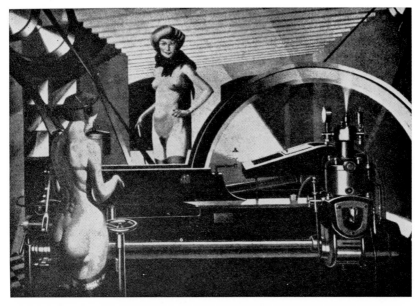

Fig. 7. The fundamental incongruity between technology and human nature was allegorized by the German artist Georg Scholz (1896-1942) in his composition "Flesh and Iron."

fundamental incongruity between technology and human nature was allegorized in 1914 by the German artist Georg Scholz in a composition "Flesh and Iron." In this picture the artist expressed his feeling of the incommensurability of the two women whom he placed in juxtaposition to a machine. In 1950, Pablo Picasso presented his own version of Courbet's "Les desmoiselles" of 1856: he showed the two young girls fragmented, like pieces of a jigsaw puzzle which defy all efforts towards integration into normal human beings. George Tooker, an exponent of the U.S. "Sharp Focus School" of the post-World War II period, uses a carefullly realistic technique to allegorize the artificiality, drabness and depersonalization of life in the "megalopolis" which calls for an entirely new approach to the problem of leisure time activities and recreation.

A sense of total dissolution of form and content in art is conveyed in "abstract painting" with its disregard of tradition, its totalitarian claims for recognition and its intolerance of criticism.

Fig. 8. George Tooker (born 1920), an exponent of the U.S. "Sharp Focus School" of the post-World War II period uses in his painting "Megalopolis" a carefully realistic technique to emphasize the artificiality, drabness and depersonalization of life in the Big City.

Hans Hofmann's picture "Emerald Isle" was recently described as the "work of an old master in modern art." Ortega y Gasset has appropriately spoken of the new style which it represents as being indicative of a "dehumanization of art."

This is how the philosopher Houston Smith of the Massachusetts Institute of Technology expressed himself on the subject:

"As long as reality was conceived as a great chain of being—a hierarchy of worth descending from God as its crown through angels, men, animals and plants to inanimate objects at the base —it could be reasonably argued that great art should attend to great subjects: Scenes from the Gospels, major battles or distinguished lords or ladies.

With cubism and surrealism, the distinction between trivial and

Fig. 9. A sense of total dissolution of form and content in art is conveyed in "abstract painting" with its disregard of tradition, its totalitarian claims for recognition and its intolerance of criticism. Hans Hofmann's (born 1908) picture "Esmerald Isle" was recently described as the "work of an old master in modern art." Ortega y Gasset has appropriately spoken of the new style which it represents as being indicative of a "dehumanization of art."

Fig. 10. In his sketches and paintings Hieronymus Bosch's phantasy created an imaginative world of his own though he never deviated from reality. Bosch depicted scenes that no mortal had ever seen. But he did so by synthesizing patterns from ingredients known to everybody from our common environment. E.g., he arranged into new combinations human

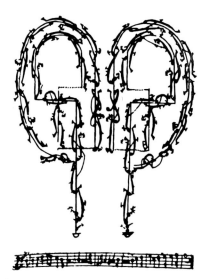

Fig. 11. A long tradition in the notation of movements has been established in choreography even though no standardization of graphic presentation has yet been reached. The above sketch showing steps of a 17th century dance by Raoul Feuillet (1675-1730) indicates positioning and directives for the dances in timed relationship to a simple melodic sequence.

bodies, fishing rods, beer barrels, sticks, wheels, bags, feet and head of a rooster, pieces of a gallows, a sailing boat and a ladder. In one of his paintings he depicted a man's body covered with fish scales and gave him a bird's head with ostrich plumes; seaweed sprouted wings and an octopus became a mammal. Phantasms and hybrid monsters armed with swords, harpoons and knives appeared and thus the artist gives to each of his creations a weird life of its own. Many of Bosch's pictures engender an atmosphere of enigmatic unreality. Still, everything remains recognizable and identifiable. Even where he transcends the boundaries of our everyday world, he never becomes "inhuman," to use the term which Ortega y Gasset has introduced in his critical interpretation of contemporary art.

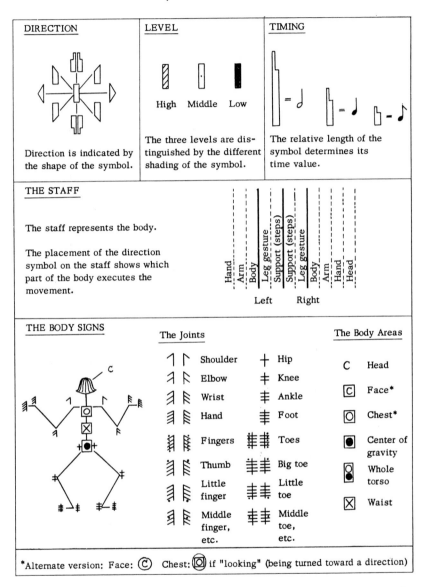

DIRECTION

Direction is indicated by the shape of the symbol.

LEVEL

High   Middle   Low

The three levels are distinguished by the different shading of the symbol.

TIMING

The relative length of the symbol determines its time value.

THE STAFF

The staff represents the body.

The placement of the direction symbol on the staff shows which part of the body executes the movement.

Hand | Arm | Body | Leg gesture | Support (steps) | Support (steps) | Leg gesture | Body | Arm | Hand | Head

Left   Right

THE BODY SIGNS

The Joints

Shoulder	Hip	C	Head
Elbow	Knee	C	Face*
Wrist	Ankle	O	Chest*
Hand	Foot	●	Center of gravity
Fingers	Toes		Whole torso
Thumb	Big toe		
Little finger	Little toe	X	Waist
Middle finger, etc.	Middle toe, etc.		

The Body Areas

*Alternate version: Face: Ⓒ   Chest: if "looking" (being turned toward a direction)

Fig. 12. One of the most elaborate efforts towards the introduction of a universally usable system of staff notation was made by Rudolph Laban whose life's work has been described in a book by Ann Hutchinson entitled "Labanotations." (cp. Ann Hutchinson.: *Labanotation.* New York, Laughlin, 1954.)

Fig. 13. The majority of textbooks on athletics, physical education and gymnastics still resort to sketches of sequential movement progressions of which the above illustrations of exercises on the sidehorse (above), the parallel bars (middle) and the horizontal bar (below) for a national competition are examples. The task confronting those who try to arrive at a more advanced system of notation of movement is to translate drawings of this kind into symbolic abstractions, comparable to the form design evolved three centuries ago in musical staff notation.

important disappears. Alarm clocks, driftwood, pieces of broken glass become appropriate subjects for the most monumental paintings."

A penetrating comment on the issue under reference is contained in Sir Charles Sherrington's book *Man on his Nature.* The human mind, Sherrington said, can fathom the external world only in meaningful images. When Socrates spoke of his desire to "go to the other world" to see there "an earthly love, or wife, or son and conversing with them," he remarked that he would be infinitely delighted to be able to talk to Odysseus and to the

Fig. 14.

Figs. 14 and 15. A problem with which choreography has been confronted for a long time and which has assumed importance in physical education and gymnastics is that of providing for position patterns of participants in group and mass gymnastic displays. Figure 14 depicts a scene from a recent Sokol festival in Prague, Czechsolovakia in which 15,000 participants performed. Figure 15 shows the starting positions of the vast masses from which the circular and triangular groupings in Figure 14 originated.

leaders of the Trojan expedition. "To imagine Paradise," Sherrington observed, "a lofty mind thus invokes its favorite pursuit from earth and custom of earth's social creature, man. Mind's earthliness innately shapes all it does, perhaps most so when it tries to be unearthly."

The 16th Century painter Hieronymus Bosch was greatly interested about the "Evil One" and about "transmundane demons." Yet his vision could achieve nothing to the purpose beyond contriving ugly hybrids from familiar shapes of terrestrial creation. Nor could the noble imagination of Dante transcend the limits

Půdorys č. 15

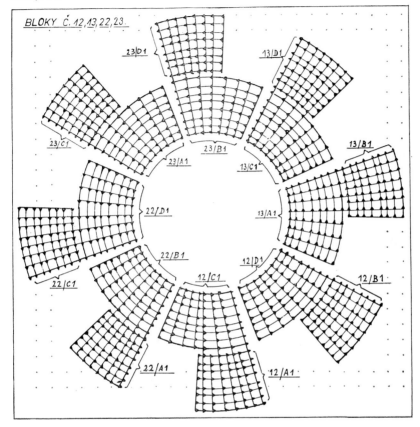

Hlavní tribuna

Fig. 15.

of actual experience: when the poet traveled the Inferno, Purgatory and Paradise, "he still walked Italy, the Italy he loved and grieved for."

ESTHETIC EVALUATION OF HUMAN MOVEMENTS

One of the great cultural attributes of sport is that it creates beauty. The esthetic value of human movements engendered in sport is synonymous with that which emanates from art at its best. Maheu believes that the beauty which sports begets, "is

Fig. 16. Joan Benesch of the Sadler's Wells Ballet has devised a system of dance notation "based on what the eye actually sees, a draftsman's shorthand as it were." Positions and movements are written down on musical staves, so as to fit into the time pattern of the staff notation for the orchestral score. (Rudolph and Joan Benesch.: *An Introduction to Benesch Dance Notation.* New York, Pitman, 1956.)

immanent in the very act which creates it." The two, he thinks, are inseparable from the fleeting moment. He therefore conceives a contrast between the beauty of sport and the beauty of art. "Art expresses itself through signs, through stylization, not of things, not of body or of living creatures." Art places a distance between the object and the creation of beauty. For Maheu, signs and symbols are the substance of art; while the substance of sport is the living body itself. Sport belongs wholly to the present, the actor merging completely with the action.* The same synonymity, he feels, is not possible in art whose objects are connected with the finished work by a relationship of meaning, a relationship that is arbitrary, removed from natural contacts. This characterization, Maheu holds, applies alike to the man of letters and the writer who do not work with emotions or ideas or passions but with words; to the painter who works with colors and light effects which represent or can represent other things or objects; though for him the sign is all important. Even in sculpture and in music, it is the sign that counts.

"Between the creator and the object he creates is fixed that distance which liberates art and endows it with its quality of eternity. Sport consists wholly of action; art, on the contrary, by its employment of the sign which freed it from the object and from life, moves into eternity. Thus, sport and art face in opposite directions."

Maheu concludes that sport cannot as yet give us what we are offered by artistic expression and culture, namely a meaning which enables us to transcend the temporary, to transcend all that is ephemeral, and to discover something of eternal value. But he is confident that one day sport will cross the threshold and that a true element of culture will emerge from it.

---

* S. Wenkart is in agreement with Maheu's viewpoint: "In the transition from subject to object there is a complete elimination of schisms, and an existential experience of oneness." (cp. Simon Wenkart: "The Meaning of Sports for Contemporary Man." Journal of Existential Psychiatry, Vol. III, No. 12, Spring 1963. pp. 397-405)

Are we in fact justified in thus separating the esthetic manifestations of sport from those of the arts? Is the beauty that is derived from ice skating and dancing, from gymnastics and water diving, from soccer, hockey and horse back riding categorically different from that of, say, music and of the stage? Is it true that only in sport the beauty which the performer's action begets is immanent in the very act which creates it? I believe that the answer to these questions is in the negative. The esthetic implications of the acts that engender beauty in sport are fundamentally the same as the acts that engender beauty in music and on the stage. They all belong to the present, so as Maheu has rightly pointed out in respect of sport. Like the performing athlete, the performing musician and the performing actor merge completely with their action. Esthetics in sport and esthetics in music and on the stage also have the same double character in that on the one hand they appeal but for a "fleeting moment"; while on the other their performances can be rendered permanent: in music through staff notation, in literature through the written word; in sport through graphic symbolization, e.g., in choreography. All these forms of esthetic revelation can therefore be reflected upon and repeated; all three thus attain a quality of the "eternal."

MOTOR NOTATION

Though the development of systems of notation of movements in sport is not as far advanced as that of notation of music and literature, sufficient progress has already been made in the symbolization of the dance, of calisthenics, of gymnastics and of other activities to justify the statement that sport has crossed the threshold of which Maheu has spoken; and that for this reason alone it moves towards the emergence of a new and dynamic cultural force.

SPORT AS CREATOR OF MYTHS

Like the arts, sport is a creator of myths and imagery. Athletic champions of the past appear in retrospect greater than their heirs do at present, even though the evidence proves the contrary conclusion to be justified. In the mind of those of us who competed many years ago in athletic contests, the memory of our triumphs remains vivid and may even shine brighter as time passes on.

The desire to create myths in sport often overrules scientific considerations. In 1957, a group of eminent American physicians met at Peter Bent Brigham Hospital in Massachusetts to discuss medical observations made during the Boston marathon race. A psychiatrist proclaimed that "death may be the vague ultimate aim of marathon runners"; that these athletes "always run to the point of utter exhaustion and into collapse," like the King's messenger of old who took pride in sacrificing themselves for their master. He went on quoting from Robert Browning's poem "Incident of the French Camp" which describes how a runner brought news from a distant battle to Napoleon. No sooner was the message delivered than he perished:

> "You're wounded!" "Nay," the soldier's pride
> Touched to the quick, he said:
> "I'm kill'd, Sire!" And the chief beside
> Smiling the boy fell dead."

"One always sees in these messengers a moment of exaltation," the psychiatrist continued, "when they have finally won through and delivered the news; then it seems to be an almost inexorable destiny for them to drop dead—anything but death would be a dull, sodden, anticlimax."

In conclusion he alluded to the mythological story of Icarus, "that high flyer who soared upward until he nearly reached the sun inspite of the warning of his father Daedalus":

> "Alas! The sun's heat melted the waxen wings, and he plummeted into the seas. This rise to triumph followed almost at once by the fall to death may bear some kinship to the kind of drama that seems to unfold in the ancient messenger or the marathon runner."

The learned audience received this imaginative effort of phantasy on the part of the psychiatrist with considerable appreciation. The *New England Journal of Medicine* referred to it in an editorial article which was entitled "Icarus Complex." *The fact that nobody has ever died from marathon running was completely lost behind the allegorical clouds raised by the inspired myth.*

Of course mythology and allegorization, symbolic allusion and simile have at times been interwoven with fruitful scientific theorizing—but fruitful only if the iron rules of interplay of imagination and verification were observed. Paul Ehrlich invoked the medieval symbol of the "magic bullet" while he demonstrated the capacity of selected chemical compounds to combine with specific pathogenic microorganisms. Freud introduced terms like "Oedipus complex" in an effort to identify certain psychological constellations that, he held, characterize the conditio humana; and from the colorless world of the Hades of ancient Hellas he brought back into the light of the 20th Century the shadows of Agamemnon, Electra and Orestes.

All creative human endeavors—among them the natural sciences and the arts—have engendered their own mythology.* In as far as sport has shown itself possessed by powers of a like kind, it has revealed equivalent creative potentialities.

Sport is one of the avenues of mankind's never ceasing strive for excellence. Its uniqueness lies in the intimacy between the physical happenings of our bodies and their repercussions in our minds; as well as in the general recognizability of the social and esthetic values which sport engenders. Sport evokes experiences that are exclusively human and independent of the changing forms, patterns and customs of a civilization which involves profoundly modifying components of our environment. The anthropological relevance of this differential interrelationship has been shown by Erwin Straus in his essay *The Upright Posture,* which as he puts it, reflects the unchangeable and pre-arranged material framework of human existence, in contrast to the changeability of the world around us. The concern of physical culture with the cultivation and improvement of the individual's own motor resources relates to both the body and the mind from which it originates.

"The ethics of sport" Maheu writes, "proclaim the dignity of the body and deny that there can be any possible comparison between the machine that is the human body and a machine fashioned by man, or even any comparison, as Jean Prevost has said, between the skill and strength of an animal and the skill and strength of man."

---

* cp. also Peter G. M. Dawe, "Mind and Machine," Listener, Oct. 17, 1963, 591f.

POETIC INTERPRETATION OF SPORT AND PLAY

The phenomenological meaning of the terms sport, play and game have changed in the course of time. For centuries poets have given metaphoric expression to their awareness that sport contains elements of experiences which are absent in ordinary life.

In his "Fairie Queen," Edmund Spenser dwelt upon the problem of unpredictability or, as he preferred to call it, "mutability" in play.

"What man that sees the ever-whirling wheel
Of change, the which all mortal things doth sway,
But that thereby doth find, and plainly feel,
How mutability in them doth play
Her cruel sports to many men's decay?"

In Shakespeare's Othello, Iago refers to his general's love for Desdemona:
"She is sport for Jove."

Play can remove the pressure of anxiety and in doing so alter the sense of time. In *A Midsummer Night's Dream,* Theseus asks:
"Is there no play to ease the anguish of a torturing hour?"

The quality of the exceptional, of the festive and of the enjoyable that is attached to sport at its best, is revealed in the following lines spoken by the Prince in King Henry IV:
"If all the year were playing holidays,
To sport would be as tedious as to work;
But when they seldom come, they wish'd for come."

Play's combination of reality and phantasy creates an enclave whose boundaries are delineated against the drab territory in which daily life takes its course. Also, play's appeal is universal and independent of time and place.

Cassius: How many ages hence
   Shall this our lofty scene be acted o'er
   In states unborn and accents yet unknown.
Brutus: How many times shall Caesar bleed in sport.
      (Julius Caesar)

In his *Tale of a Tub,* Ben Jonson speaks of the sports of love:
"Come, my Celia, let us prove
while we can the sports of love."

The same metaphor appears in John Milton's *Lycidus*:
"Alas! What boots it with uncessant care
To tend the homely, slighted, shepherd's trade,
And strictly meditate the thankless Muse?
Were it not better done, as others use,
To sport with Amaryllis in the shade,
Or with the tangles of Neaera's hair."

and more lately in a poem by Robert Bridges:
I hear a linnet courting
His lady in the spring;
His mates were idly sporting,
Nor stayed to hear him sing
 His song of love.—
I fear my speech distorting
His tender love.
I heard a linnet courting.

Jane Austen refers in *Pride and Prejudice* to the unpredictability of the continuous interplay between man and his neighbors.
"For what do we live but to make sport of our
neighbors and laugh at them in our turn?"

while the following four lines appear in Matthew Arnold's *Emped-
ocles on Etna:*
"Nature, with equal mind
Sees all her sons at play,
Sees man control the wind,
The wind sweeps man away,"

CONCLUDING REMARKS

In many ways the humanistic and sociological functions of sport
as leisure are synonymous with those of art. Both, sport and art
are means of modifying and enriching man's experiences.* In
his lecture "On Actors and Acting," Max Reinhardt said that the
immortality of the theater is derived from the eternal longing of

---

* "The purpose of the universe is play. The artists know that play and art and
creation are different names for the same thing—a thing that is sweats and agonies
and ecstasies. The artists who know more than anyone else about play which is art,
which is creation, must be the leaders and guides." (Don Marquis)

the human mind to be transformed. This statement equally applies to sport, as Maheu has also recognized. We all, Reinhardt wrote, carry in us the capacity of experiencing every conceivable emotion. Nothing human is foreign to us. If it were different, we would be unable to understand each other, in life as well as in art which renders possible the projection of latent feelings and moods and thoughts in their concealed diversity. All this is true also for sport as a medium of communication of unlimited range and appeal; perhaps even more so than for art whose appeal is selective. Thus Max Reinhardt's dictum that immortality has been bestowed upon the theater because of the ever present desire of the human mind to be transformed applies still more ubiquitously to play and game and sport.

The French poet Paul Valery wrote that all human cultures, religious and metaphysical systems are "play," in that they represent but potentialities of conceptual thinking, sketches of a power of the mind that can be projected into reality. But they can also be withdrawn; every culture is mortal as the study of history has taught. The culture of sport, however, is projected primarily into ourselves. Its universal human reverberation is derived therefrom. It can thus be explained that once again the Olympic ideal appeals today to all people, so as it appealed almost 3000 years ago to the people of Greece at the height of Hellenistic civilization. Sport renders accessible to us mobilization of elements of which other cultural manifestations do not partake. Sport as leisure enables man to discover and develop cultural resources which are hidden in himself.

REFERENCES

Grazia, Sebastian de: *Of Time, Work and Leisure.* Twentieth Century Fund, 1962.

Jokl, Ernst: Uber den Aufbau der menschlichen Leistung. Theorie und Praxis der Korperkultur, No. 11/12, 1961.

Kerr, Walter: *The Decline of Pleasure.* Simon & Schuster, 1962.

Kraus, Hans and Wilhelm Raab: *Hypokinetic Disease.* Thomas, Springfield, 1961.

Maheu, Rene: Sport and Culture. UNESCO. *International Journal of Adult and Youth Education,* Vol. XIV, No. 4, 1962.

Mumford, Lewis: *The Culture of Cities.* London, Secker & Warburg, 1940.

Noel-Baker, Philip: Sport and International Understanding. UNESCO. *International Journal of Adult and Youth Education,* Vol. *XIV,* No. 4, 1962.

Ortega y Gasset: *The Dehumanization of Art.* Doubleday, Garden City, New York, 1956.

Plessner, Helmut: *Die Funktion des Sports in der industriellen Gesellschaft.* Wissenschaft und Weltbild, December 1956.

Russell, Bertrand: *In Praise of Idleness.* London, George Allen & Unwin Ltd., 1935.

Sherrington, Sir Charles: *Man on his Nature.* Cambridge, University Press, 1940.

Straus, Erwin: The Upright Posture. *Psychiat. Quart.,* 26:529, 1952.

MEDICAL SOCIOLOGY OF SPORT

INTRODUCTION

AT THE 15th Olympic Games in Helsinki, Finland, in the summer of 1952, 69 nations were represented by teams of competitors. The total number of athletes entered for the various events amounted to 4,925.

Of 60 countries which in 1952 were members of the United Nations 42 came to the Olympic Games. As Table I[1] indicates, 18 member countries of the United Nations failed to send teams, namely Afghanistan, Bolivia, Colombia, Costa Rica, Dominican Republic, Ecuador, El Salvador, Ethiopia, Haiti, Honduras, Iraq, Liberia, Nicaragua, Paraguay, Peru, Saudi Arabia, Syria and Yemen. On the other hand 29 teams had been entered by countries and separate regions which did not belong to the United Nations, namely Austria, Bahama, Bermuda, British Guiana, Bulgaria, Ceylon, Finland, Germany, Gold Coast, Hong Kong, Hungary, Ireland, Italy, Jamaica, Japan, Korea, Liechtenstein, Monaco, Netherlands' Antilles, Nigeria, Portugal, Puerto Rico, Rumania, Saar, Singapore, Spain, Switzerland, Trinidad and Tobago and Viet-Nam. The absence of a full team from the People's Republic of China and of representation from East Germany were noted with regret at Helsinki. Of the above named countries, 10 have in the ensuing 4 years been allowed to join the United Nations, namely Austria, Bulgaria, Ceylon, Finland, Hungary, Ireland, Italy, Portugal, Rumania and Spain. Two of the major athletic powers of the world, namely Germany—both the German Federal Republic, or West Germany, and the German Democratic Republic, or East Germany—, and Japan, as well as the People's Republic of China still were not attached to the

---

[1] Yearbook of UN, pp. 840, 841.

Medical Sociology of Sport

TABLE 1

PARTICIPATION OF DIFFERENT COUNTRIES AND REGIONS IN OLYMPIC GAMES

* = no Unesco publications distributor in the country o = elected U.N. member since 1952	Participating in 1952 Olympic Games		Not Participating
	Man and Woman Athletes	Man Athletes Only	
Members of the United Nations in 1952	Argentina Australia Belgium Brazil Byelorussian SSR* Canada Chile Czechoslovakia Denmark France Guatemala* India Israel Mexico Netherlands New Zealand Norway Panama Poland* Sweden Ukrainian SSR* Union of South Africa United Kingdom United States of America USSR* Uruguay Venezuela Yugoslavia Total population 1 084 mill.	Burma China Cuba Egypt Greece Iceland* Indonesia Iran Lebanon Luxembourg Pakistan Philippines Thailand Turkey Total population 757 mill.	Afghanistan* Bolivia Colombia Costa Rica Dominican Republic Ecuador El Salvador* Ethiopia Haiti Honduras* Iraq Liberia Nicaragua* Paraguay Peru Saudi Arabia* Syria* Yemen* Total population 89 mil.

Table 1 cont'd

* = no Unesco publications distributor in the country o = elected U.N. member since 1952	Participating in 1952 Olympic Games		Not Participating
	Man and Woman Athletes	Man Athletes Only	
Members of the U.N. specialized agencies only in 1952	oAustria oBulgaria* oFinland Germany oHungary oItaly Japan Korea oPortugal oRumania* Switzerland Total population 291 mill.	oCeylon oIreland* Monaco* oSpain Viet-Nam Total population 66 mill.	oAlbania* oCambodia oJordan oLaos* oLibya* oNepal* San Marino* Vatican City* Total population 16 mill.
Countries and separate regions which in 1952 were not members of the United Nations nor of the U.N. specialized agencies	Bermuda* Hong Kong Jamaica Saar* Singapore Total population 6 mill.	Bahama* British Guiana* Gold Coast* Liechtenstein* Netherlands' Antilles* Nigeria Puerto Rico Trinidad and Tobago* Total population 37 mill.	Andorra* Anglo-Egyptian Sudan* Bhutan* Eritrea* Malayan Federation Maldives* Mongolian People's Republic* Tanger Trieste* Total population 17 mill.
	1 381 mill. 2 241 mill.	860 mill.	122 mill. + total population of colonies 124 mill. = 246 mill. ∼ 10 per cent of world population

United Nations though they are affiliated to the International Olympic Committee. Japan became a member of the United Nations on December 18, 1956.

In accordance with the total population figures of the countries which sent teams to the 1952 Games in Helsinki, *90 per cent of the inhabitants of the world were represented.*

The USSR entered a single team though it is represented at the United Nations by three political entities, namely USSR, Byelorussian SSR and Ukrainian SSR. On the other hand, the former Dominions of the British Empire, *i.e.*, Canada, Ceylon, Australia, New Zealand, India, Pakistan and Union of South Africa, each of whom is separately accredited to the UN, came as independent national units. Moreover, the Colonial Office had facilitated the entry of separate teams from Bahama, Bermuda, Burma, British Guiana, Gold Coast, Hong Kong, Jamaica, Nigeria, Singapore and Trinidad, thus demonstrating its desire to assist the different societies under the British Crown to be guided towards civic and political autonomy.* No corresponding trend was in evidence as far as the other major colonial powers were concerned. In the light of subsequent developments it is worth mentioning that no national teams were entered for Algiers, Morocco and Tunis nor for the other French-governed overseas countries, and that such territories as Portuguese Angola and Mozambique, Belgian Congo and Ruanda-Urundi, and Spanish North and West Africa did not make their appearance at the Games as separate units. By contrast the Netherlands had given active assistance to the dispatch of a team from the Netherlands' Antilles.

The Saar sent its own team though subsequently the Olympic Committee of this small West European region has joined the Olympic Committee of the Federal Republic of Germany.

None of the Trust Territories under the United Nations Assembly's control, *i.e.*, Cameroons, Ruanda-Urundi, Somaliland, Tanganyika, Togoland, Nauru, New Guinea, Pacific Islands and Western Samoa were represented at the Games; nor had South West Africa entered a team. Considering the fact that the United

---

* The Malay States, Barbados, Malta, the Leeward and Windward Islands and the Caribbean Federation were subsequently given a larger scope political autonomy and enabled to enter their own athletic teams.

Nations have accepted responsibility for the care of the former and South Africa, also a member of the United Nations, for the latter, this is a matter of considerable concern. It was felt at the time that the question of the establishment of National Olympic Committees in these territories ought to be taken up by the Trusteeship Council of the United Nations.[2]

A comment is appropriate on the presence in the United States team of white, black and yellow-brown athletes. The moral and social implications of the successful integration of so different ethnic groups within a single national team are far reaching in that they indicate the extent to which the letter of the liberal constitution of the Unites States has become law. In Table 2, the contributions of the black and yellow-brown athletes to the total athletic achievement pool of the United States are shown—both in extent and in quality they are equally impressive. According to Myrdal's survey[3] less than 10 per cent of the population of America are coloured, but the share of points contributed by the United States' black men and women was 20 per cent of the total allocation of points for the whole team. Of the remaining 80 per cent, a substantial share stands to the credit of yellow-brown athletes.

It is interesting to speculate on the latent athletic all-round potential of a highly developed and industrialized country like South Africa whose 9 million black and ½ million Indian and Chinese citizens did not compete at Olympic Games.

The yellow-brown population block of the USSR which amounts to about 17 million[4] did not seem to be represented at Helsinki.

Tables 3[5] and 4 allow an analysis of the nations of the world in terms of their participation at the Games as well as in terms of the inclusion in the Olympic teams of women. The maximal number of competitors allowed to each country at the Summer Games in individual sports was 180 for men and 53 for women. The corresponding figures for team events was 31 men's teams and 3 women's teams. On the whole the number of woman competi-

[2] Yearbook of UN 1953, p. 36.
[3] Myrdal, 1944.
[4] Statistical Yearbook of Finland, 1955, p. 332.
[5] Kolkka, 1955, pp. 244, 245.

Medical Sociology of Sport

TABLE 2

CONTRIBUTION OF THE DIFFERENT RACES TO THE POINT SHARE. INDIVIDUAL COMPETITION

Country	Point Share				%				Point Level*)			
	White	Yellow-brown	Black	Total	White	Yellow-brown	Black	Total	White	Yellow-brown	Black	Total
1. United States	6 852	351	1 813	9 016	76	4	20	100	42.3	87.8	64.8	46.8
2. USSR	8 690	.	.	8 690	100	.	.	100	41.6	.	.	41.6
3. Sweden	5 253	.	.	5 253	100	.	.	100	34.8	.	.	34.8
4. Hungary	4 726	.	.	4 726	100	.	.	100	37.8	.	.	37.8
5. Germany	4 486	.	.	4 486	100	.	.	100	32.3	.	.	32.3
6. Finland	4 436	.	.	4 436	100	.	.	100	24.8	.	.	24.8
7. Great Britain	4 243	.	149	4 392	97	.	3	100	24.0	.	49.7	24.4
8. France	3 719	.	139	3 858	96	.	4	100	23.0	.	19.9	22.8
9. Italy	3 610	.	.	3 610	100	.	.	100	29.3	.	.	29.3
10. Czechoslovakia	2 386	.	.	2 386	100	.	.	100	33.6	.	.	33.6
11. Australia	2 172	.	.	2 172	100	.	.	100	29.4	.	.	29.4
12. Switzerland	1 962	.	.	1 962	100	.	.	100	18.7	.	.	18.7
13. South Africa	1 878	.	.	1 878	100	.	.	100	33.5	.	.	33.5
14. Argentina	1 703	.	111	1 814	94	.	6	100	22.4	.	55.6	23.3
15. Japan	.	1 791	.	1 791	.	100	.	100	.	28.0	.	28.0
16. Denmark	1 664	.	.	1 664	100	.	.	100	22.5	.	.	22.5
17. Canada	1 626	.	21	1 647	99	.	1	100	19.8	.	21.0	19.8
18. Holland	1 573	.	.	1 573	100	.	.	100	26.7	.	.	26.7
19. Rumania	1 530	.	.	1 530	100	.	.	100	20.1	.	.	20.1
20. Norway	1 522	.	.	1 522	100	.	.	100	19.3	.	.	19.3
21. Poland	1 477	.	.	1 477	100	.	.	100	17.5	.	.	17.5
22. Belguim	1 347	.	.	1 347	100	.	.	100	18.2	.	.	18.2
23. Brazil	818	101	367	1 286	64	8	28	100	17.0	50.5	33.4	21.1
24. Egypt	1 258	.	.	1 258	100	.	.	100	17.2	.	.	17.2
25. Austria	1 206	.	.	1 206	100	.	.	100	17.7	.	.	17.7
26. Mexico	894	.	.	894	100	.	.	100	17.9	.	.	17.9
27. Iran	849	.	.	849	100	.	.	100	38.6	.	.	38.6
28. Yugoslavia	832	.	.	832	100	.	.	100	15.7	.	.	15.7
29. Turkey	755	.	.	755	100	.	.	100	24.4	.	.	24.4
30. Bulgaria	659	.	.	659	100	.	.	100	18.3	.	.	18.3
31. India	553	.	.	553	100	.	.	100	14.9	.	.	14.9
32. Jamaica	.	.	542	542	.	.	100	100	.	.	45.2	45.2
33. Chile	535	.	.	535	100	.	.	100	15.3	.	.	15.3
34. Luxembourg	506	.	.	506	100	.	.	100	16.3	.	.	16.3
35. Portugal	499	.	.	499	100	.	.	100	10.6	.	.	10.6

Country	Point Share				%				Point Level*)			
	White	*Yellow-brown*	*Black*	*Total*	*White*	*Yellow-brown*	*Black*	*Total*	*White*	*Yellow-brown*	*Black*	*Total*
36. Venezuela	386	.	99	485	80	.	20	100	10.2	.	14.1	10.8
37. Korea	.	447	.	447	.	100	.	100	.	29.8	.	29.8
38. New Zealand	429	.	.	429	100	.	.	100	35.8	.	.	35.8
39. Spain	359	.	.	359	100	.	.	100	21.1	.	.	21.1
40. Cuba	157	.	185	342	46	.	54	100	14.3	.	20.6	17.1
41. Iceland	338	.	.	338	100	.	.	100	16.1	.	.	16.1
42. Greece	301	.	.	301	100	.	.	100	12.0	.	.	12.0
43. Philippines	118	178	.	296	40	60	.	100	19.7	19.8	.	19.7
44. Guatemala	203	.	52	255	80	.	20	100	9.2	.	8.7	9.1
45. Lebanon	255	.	.	255	100	.	.	100	28.3	.	.	28.3
46. Saar	255	.	.	255	100	.	.	100	9.1	.	.	9.1
47. Pakistan	252	.	.	252	100	.	.	100	9.0	.	.	9.0
48. Puerto Rico	236	.	.	236	100	.	.	100	11.2	.	.	11.2
49. Israel	182	.	.	182	100	.	.	100	9.6	.	.	9.6
50. Uruguay	182	.	.	182	100	.	.	100	11.4	.	.	11.4
51. Nigeria	.	.	146	146	.	.	100	100	.	.	13.3	13.3
52. Trinidad	.	.	127	127	.	.	100	100	.	.	42.3	42.3
53. Iceland	120	.	.	120	100	.	.	100	8.6	.	.	8.6
54. Hong Kong	22	95	.	117	19	81	.	100	11.0	13.6	.	13.0
55. Bermuda	104	.	8	112	93	.	7	100	9.5	.	8	9.3
56. Singapore	18	87	.	105	17	83	.	100	9.0	17.4	.	15.0
57. Thailand	90	10	.	100	90	10	.	100	8.2	10.0	.	8.3
58. Burma	.	74	.	74	.	100	.	100	.	14.8	.	14.8
59. Ceylon	69	.	.	69	100	.	.	100	11.5	.	.	11.5
60. Indonesia	34	23	.	57	60	40	.	100	34.0	11.5	.	19.0
61. Gold Coast	.	.	49	49	.	.	100	100	.	.	9.8	9.8
62. Monaco	39	.	.	39	100	.	.	100	4.9	.	.	4.9
63. Viet-Nam	14	24	.	38	37	63	.	100	7.0	4.8	.	5.4
64. Liechtenstein	17	.	.	17	100	.	.	100	8.5	.	.	8.5
65. China	.	11	.	11	.	100	.	100	.	11.0	.	11.0
66. British Guiana	8	.	.	8	100	.	.	100	8.0	.	.	8.0
67. Panama	.	.	.	.	100	.	.	100	—	.	.	—
Total	80 407	3 192	3 808	87 407	92	4	4	100	25.1	26.6	37.3	25.5

) Definition of point level on p. 61.

TABLE 3
NUMBER OF COMPETITORS IN DIFFERENT SPORTS EVENTS

Country	Shooting	Football	Basketball	Hockey	Canoeing Men	Canoeing Women	Fencing Men	Fencing Women	Modern Pentathlon	Boxing	Wrestling	Weight-lifting	Yachting Men	Yachting Women	Cycling	Equestrian Men	Equestrian Women	Rowing	Swimming Men	Swimming Women	Gymnastics Men	Gymnastics Women	Athletics Men	Athletics Women	Men—Total	Women—Total	Grand Totals
Argentina	7	—	14	—	—	—	10	—	3	10	6	5	14	—	6	6	—	9	16	1	2	—	10	6	118	8	126
Australia	3	11	—	—	—	—	4	1	1	5	4	3	6	—	6	—	—	12	15	4	—	—	13	4	69	10	79
Austria	—	—	—	11	6	1	5	2	—	4	3	4	3	—	4	—	—	4	15	2	8	8	8	6	89	20	109
Bahamas	—	—	—	—	—	—	—	—	—	—	—	—	7	—	—	—	—	—	—	—	—	—	—	—	7	—	7
Belgium	4	11	13	11	4	—	14	3	1	5	9	2	4	—	11	4	—	12	15	5	3	—	21	—	129	5	134
Bermuda	—	—	—	—	—	—	—	—	—	—	—	—	—	—	—	—	—	—	4	—	—	—	—	2	4	2	6
Brazil	8	11	13	—	—	—	5	—	3	6	—	3	6	—	—	—	—	3	23	2	—	—	7	3	92	5	97
British Guiana	—	—	—	—	—	—	—	—	—	—	—	1	—	—	—	—	—	—	—	—	—	—	—	—	1	—	1
Bulgaria	6	11	14	—	—	—	—	—	—	4	—	—	—	—	5	—	—	—	—	—	8	8	3	1	54	9	63
Burma	—	—	—	—	—	—	—	—	—	3	—	2	—	—	—	—	—	—	—	—	—	—	—	—	5	—	5
Canada	4	—	13	—	11	—	2	—	—	7	4	5	11	—	2	3	—	15	5	4	—	—	16	6	98	10	108
Ceylon	—	—	—	—	—	—	—	—	—	2	—	—	—	—	—	—	—	—	2	—	—	—	1	—	5	—	5
Chile	2	11	13	—	—	—	—	—	3	—	—	—	—	—	4	3	—	1	1	—	—	—	11	2	55	2	57
China	—	—	—	—	—	—	—	—	—	—	—	—	—	—	—	—	—	1	—	—	—	—	—	—	1	—	1
Cuba	2	—	12	—	—	—	1	—	—	—	—	1	3	—	—	—	—	—	2	—	3	—	5	—	29	—	29
Czechoslovakia	6	—	14	—	12	1	9	3	—	5	4	4	7	—	6	4	1	8	4	—	8	8	16	4	87	13	100
Denmark	5	—	14	—	8	1	8	—	3	5	5	3	—	—	13	3	—	25	3	—	7	—	10	1	115	14	129
Egypt	6	12	14	11	—	—	8	3	3	7	12	6	—	—	—	3	—	8	15	—	8	—	7	—	106	—	106
Finland	11	11	14	13	9	—	—	3	3	10	16	6	14	—	11	5	—	26	11	5	8	8	56	13	230	30	260
France	9	11	14	13	12	1	18	—	3	10	10	5	9	—	10	9	—	17	12	8	8	8	43	11	213	31	244
Great Britain	12	11	—	13	6	1	14	3	3	10	6	5	14	—	12	6	1	23	22	16	6	8	50	16	213	44	257
Gold Coast	—	—	—	—	—	—	—	—	—	—	—	—	—	—	—	—	—	—	—	—	—	—	7	—	7	—	7
Germany	6	14	—	15	9	1	8	1	3	10	8	5	14	—	5	7	—	21	15	7	8	8	25	14	173	32	205
Greece	6	11	12	—	—	—	3	—	—	—	3	—	3	—	—	—	—	3	—	—	—	—	10	—	48	—	48
Guatemala	3	—	—	—	—	—	—	—	—	—	3	—	—	—	5	—	—	—	1	—	—	—	5	1	20	1	21
Hong Kong	—	—	—	—	—	—	—	—	—	—	—	—	—	—	—	—	—	—	2	2	—	—	—	—	2	2	4
Hungary	6	14	13	—	11	1	14	3	3	9	12	2	—	—	5	—	—	14	19	9	8	8	29	6	159	27	186
Iceland	—	—	—	—	—	—	—	—	—	—	—	—	—	—	—	—	—	—	—	—	—	—	8	—	8	—	8
India	2	11	—	14	—	—	—	—	—	4	4	2	—	—	5	—	—	—	10	2	2	—	6	2	60	4	64
Indonesia	—	—	—	—	—	—	—	—	—	—	—	1	—	—	—	—	—	—	1	—	—	—	1	—	3	—	3

Iran	—	—	—	—	—	—	—	—	—	6	8	7	—	—	—	—	—	—	—	—	—	—	1	—	22	—	22
Ireland	—	—	—	—	—	—	4	—	—	8	1	—	1	—	—	3	—	—	—	—	—	—	2	—	19	—	19
Israel	4	—	12	—	—	—	—	—	—	—	—	—	—	—	—	—	—	—	2	—	—	—	4	3	22	3	25
Italy	8	12	13	11	6	—	15	3	3	10	14	6	14	—	11	4	—	26	18	4	8	8	24	8	203	23	226
Jamaica	—	—	—	—	—	—	—	—	—	—	—	—	—	—	1	—	—	—	—	—	—	—	5	2	6	2	8
Japan	1	—	—	—	—	—	1	—	—	2	5	1	1	—	4	1	—	5	16	8	5	—	16	3	58	11	69
Korea	—	—	—	—	—	—	—	—	—	4	1	4	—	—	3	1	—	—	—	—	—	—	5	1	18	1	19
Lebanon	3	—	—	—	—	—	—	—	—	1	4	1	—	—	—	—	—	—	—	—	—	—	—	—	9	—	9
Liechtenstein	—	—	—	—	—	—	—	—	—	—	—	—	—	—	2	—	—	—	—	—	—	—	—	—	2	—	2
Luxembourg	—	11	—	—	4	—	4	—	—	4	3	—	—	—	4	—	—	—	1	—	6	—	7	—	44	—	44
Mexico	4	—	13	—	—	—	4	—	3	3	5	2	—	—	4	4	—	—	18	2	—	—	1	1	61	2	64
Monaco	6	—	—	—	—	—	—	—	—	—	—	—	2	—	—	—	—	—	—	—	—	—	—	—	8	—	8
Netherlands	—	11	—	11	4	1	—	—	—	5	—	2	9	—	6	3	—	12	10	12	—	8	5	5	78	26	104
Netherlands' West Indies	—	11	—	—	—	—	—	—	—	—	—	—	—	—	—	—	—	—	—	—	—	—	—	—	11	—	11
New Zealand	—	—	—	—	—	—	—	—	—	—	—	1	—	—	2	—	—	5	1	1	—	—	3	1	12	2	14
Nigeria	—	—	—	—	—	—	—	—	—	—	—	—	—	—	—	—	—	—	—	—	—	—	9	—	9	—	9
Norway	9	11	—	—	4	—	5	—	—	4	7	3	11	1	3	1	1	9	3	—	8	3	18	1	96	6	102
Pakistan	1	—	—	12	—	—	—	—	—	4	—	1	—	—	2	—	—	—	2	—	—	—	16	—	38	—	38
Panama	—	—	—	—	—	—	—	—	—	—	—	1	—	—	—	—	—	—	—	—	—	—	—	—	1	—	1
Philippines	3	—	12	—	—	—	—	—	—	5	1	2	—	—	—	—	—	—	1	—	—	—	1	—	25	—	25
Poland	2	15	—	11	—	—	10	3	—	10	5	4	—	—	—	—	—	10	6	2	8	8	20	9	101	22	123
Portugal	4	—	—	—	—	—	10		3	—	—	—	9	—	—	9	—	9	11	—	6	3	7	—	68	3	71
Puerto Rico	5	—	—	—	—	—	—	—	—	3	—	3	—	—	—	—	—	—	—	—	—	—	9	—	20	—	20
Rumania	4	11	12	—	1	—	8	—	—	10	7	4	—	—	5	6	—	9	11	—	8	8	9	3	105	11	116
Saar	2	—	—	—	2	1	5	—	—	3	3	—	—	—	—	—	—	7	1	—	6	—	2	4	31	5	36
Singapore	—	—	—	—	—	—	—	—	—	—	—	3	—	—	—	—	—	—	1	—	—	—	—	1	4	1	5
South Africa	1	—	—	—	—	—	—	—	1	8	5	4	4	—	5	—	—	5	14	1	3	—	10	3	60	4	64
Spain	4	—	—	—	—	—	—	—	—	—	—	—	1	—	—	6	—	6	9	—	1	—	—	—	27	—	27
Sweden	10	12	—	—	9	1	10	—	3	7	16	7	14	—	8	9	—	16	17	7	7	8	38	7	183	23	206
Switzerland	9	—	14	11	6	1	10	1	3	6	5	4	11	—	10	7	—	13	6	5	8	—	26	2	149	9	158
Thailand	—	—	—	—	—	—	—	—	—	—	—	—	—	—	—	—	—	—	—	—	—	—	8	—	8	—	8
Trinidad	—	—	—	—	—	—	—	—	—	—	—	2	—	—	—	—	—	—	—	—	—	—	—	—	2	—	2
Turkey	—	12	12	—	—	—	—	—	—	—	15	—	—	—	—	—	—	—	—	—	—	—	14	—	53	—	53
United States	6	11	14	—	9	—	17	3	3	10	8	7	14	2	9	8	1	26	33	18	18	8	62	9	245	41	286
Uruguay	—	—	12	—	—	—	2	—	3	2	—	—	1	—	7	—	—	3	1	—	—	—	1	1	32	1	33
USSR	11	15	14	—	12	1	13	3	3	10	16	7	14	—	10	9	—	26	30	8	8	8	57	20	255	40	295
Venezuela	7	—	—	—	—	—	8	2	—	5	3	—	—	—	4	—	—	—	2	—	—	—	7	—	36	2	38
Viet-Nam	—	—	—	—	—	—	1	—	—	2	—	—	—	—	4	—	—	—	1	—	—	—	1	—	9	—	9
Yugoslavia	6	11	—	—	1	—	—	—	—	3	3	—	3	—	—	—	—	13	12	—	8	8	17	2	77	10	87
Total	218	293	301	144	146	13	250	37	51	251	244	141	224	3	214	130	4	401	441	143	185	134	773	184	4407	518	4925

Medical Sociology of Sport

TABLE 4

PARTICIPATIONS BY COUNTRY. THE COUNTRIES
ARE LISTED IN THE ORDER OF TOTAL TEAM PARTICIPATION

Country	Men	Women	Total	Country	Men	Women	Total
1. France	29	3	32	31. Uruguay	6	—	6
2. Italy	29	3	32	32. Bulgaria	4	1	5
3. United States	29	3	32	33. Chile	5	—	5
4. USSR	29	2	31	34. Mexico	4	1	5
5. Finland	27	3	30	35. Cuba	4	—	4
6. Great Britain	27	3	30	36. India	4	—	4
7. Sweden	26	3	29	37. Spain	4	—	4
8. Germany	24	3	27	38. Venezuela	4	—	4
9. Hungary	20	2	22	39. Bahama	3	—	3
10. Switzerland	22	—	22	40. Pakistan	3	—	3
11. Denmark	2	1	21	41. Ireland	2	—	2
12. Belgium	18	1	19	42. New Zealand	2	—	2
13. Argentina	17	1	18	43. Turkey	2	—	2
14. Canada	15	2	17	44. Gold Coast	1	—	1
15. Australia	15	1	16	45. Guatemala	1	—	1
16. Netherlands	13	3	16	46. Israel	1	—	1
17. Austria	13	1	14	47. Monaco	1	—	1
18. Portugal	14	—	14	48. Netherl. Antilles	1	—	1
19. Norway	12	—	12	49. Nigeria	1	—	1
20. Poland	12	—	12	50. Philippines	1	—	1
21. Brazil	11	—	11	51. Thailand	1	—	1
22. Egypt	11	—	11				
23. Czechoslovakia	9	1	10	Total	548	42	590
24. Rumania	9	1	10				
25. Japan	7	1	8				
26. Yugoslavia	7	1	8				
27. Saar	7	1	8				
28. South Africa	8	—	8				
29. Luxembourg	7	—	7				
30. Greece	6	—	6				

tors was low, in absolute figures as well as in relation to the entry ratio for men. The policy of the International Olympic Committee implies full equality of the civic status of women. By sending woman athletes to the Games, 55 per cent of the people of the world indicated their agreement with this policy, even if it was expressed only in symbolic form, as in the case of India which delegated 7 woman participants.

Because it reflects educational patterns and evolutionary social and intellectual tendencies reference is made to Table I in which the countries are enumerated in which centers of distribution for UNESCO Publications operate. Data pertaining to participation or non-participation at the Games, and inclusion or non-inclusion of women in the respective teams at Helsinki have a distinct bearing upon the issue under analysis.

The Olympic study afforded an opportunity to test the validity of four socio-psychological postulates. First, that in the modern sports movement a highly differentiated pattern of socially and otherwise valuable activities has evolved which is acceptable to communities all over the world. Secondly, that the establishment of desirable individual and group characteristics such as those brought about by organized competitive sports is independent of language. Thirdly, that the spatial-temporal framework represented by the International Olympic Committee and its national branches is capable of attracting the enthusiasm, idealism and disciplined ambition of the entire youth of the world. Fourthly, that a number of dogmatically held concepts in the field under investigation are in need of revision, among them views held in regard to the medical implications of competitive athletics; to sports for women; to the relationship of age and fitness; and to the effect of environment and climate upon physical efficiency.

In giving rise to the evolution of a new socio-psychological technique with its manifold moral, political and cultural implications, the Olympic Games movement represents a historical advancement, and it increases the scope of freedom of the common man.

MATERIAL

The material of the study are the athletes who took part in the 1952 Olympic Games at Helsinki.

The rules of the International Olympic Committee[1] define the fundamental right of participation as follows:

1.* No discrimination is allowed against any country or person on grounds of colour, religion or politics.

— — —

6. Only nationals of a country are qualified to compete for that country in the Olympic Games.

7. Only persons who are amateurs within the definition laid down in these Rules may compete in the Olympic Games.

— — —

The Rules give the following definition of an amateur:

38. An amateur is one who participates and always has participated in sport solely for pleasure and for the physical, mental or social benefits he derives therefrom, and to whom participation in sport is nothing more than recreation without material gain of any kind direct or indirect and in accordance with the rules of the International Federation concerned.

— — —

The necessary conditions for representing a country are described as follows:

39. Only nationals of a country are eligible to represent that country in the Olympic Games. Where a competitor is a naturalized subject proof must be furnished that the competitor has always been able to comply with the definition of an amateur according to the rules prevailing in the particular sport in which the competitor wishes to take part. It is not permissible for a competitor having once represented a country in the Olympic Games to represent another country on a future occasion, except where his former country or place of birth has been incorporated in another state or if he competed for the former country because his native land had at that time no National Olympic Committee. Competitors who are citizens or subjects of a Dominion, or of a Colony belonging to a country, who were born in the Dominion or the Colony, shall be eligible to represent the Mother Country, if the Dominion or the Colony has no National Olympic Committee. Nationals of these Dominions, Colonies and the Mother Country are eligible to compete for each other's country, provided that they have lived at least five years in the Dominion, Colony or Mother Country for which they wish to compete, and provided that it is legally impossible to become a naturalized citizen of that country.

---

[1] Olympic Rules, pp. 5, 6, 18.

* The numbers of the paragraphs refer to the Charter of the Olympic Games.

Persons born abroad of parents who are nationals of another country are permitted to represent the country of the parents provided they have established their nationality and have not previously competed in the Olympic Games for the country of their birth.

Concerning the age of the competitors the Rules state:

40. There is no age limit for competitors in the Olympic Games.

The International Olympic Committee consisted at the time of the Olympic Games of the representatives of 69 participating countries (Table 1) and of the following countries which did not send any competitors:

Afghanistan	Iraq
Bolivia	Malayan Federation
Colombia	Malta
Costa Rica	Paraguay
Dominican Republic	Peru
El Salvador	Syria
Ethiopia	

Of the countries outside the International Olympic Committee none, of course, was represented at the Games.

The countries from which athletes came to take part in the Olympic Games represent a total of 2,241 million inhabitants. The summed population of the members of the International Olympic Committee which did not participate was 71 millions, and the population of the countries outside the Olympic movement was 175 millions. Thus 93 per cent of mankind had a possibility to be represented at the Games, while 90 per cent actually used it.

Data on the participants of the Olympic Games were obtained from four sources:

1. The printed *Registration forms*, which the National Olympic Committees sent to the Organizing Committee. These give the following information:

A. Country;	E. Christian names;
B. Sport;	F. Date of birth;
C. Event and sex;	G. Home address.
D. Family name;	

2. The *official list of the competition results*.[2] The list gives the name of each competitor, the country, the rank and the result in the competition.

---

[2] XV Olympia Helsinki, Bulletin No. 16.

3. Complementary information was obtained from the *official monograph of the Games*,[3] which lists the competitors in alphabetic order and tells their country, year of birth and the event in which they took part.

4. Information on race and other complementary data were obtained by *interviewing the officials* of each sport at the Games *and other experts,* and by using the *photographic material* of the Games.

Most comparisons are based on the results of the indidivual competitions only, because it was felt that the inclusion of data derived from analyses of individual and team sports in the same figure would be highly arbitrary. Some separate tables and graphs are presented for the team sports. However, the material pertaining to the team sports was not correlated with other information as extensively as were the tables referring to the individual competitions. In some events, like gymnastics, the same performance was included both in the individual and in the team evaluations. All yachting events were counted as team events, including the Olympic Dinghy Class, though it actually is an individual event.

In gymnastics, points were allocated for each individual contestant but for the twelve exercises combined, and not for each apparatus performance, in order to avoid multiplication of point credits.

The Olympic data were correlated to a number of geographical, racial, social, cultural, nutritional, and health data. The sources of the data are referred to in the appropriate chapters. Moreover, Appendix 1 lists the data used, the year to which they refer, and the sources of reference.

In some cases, decisions had to be made as to the selection of the population data. These cases are discussed in the following.

Population figures of Korea and Germany. For political reasons, the entire population of these countries could not send a representation to the Games. Nevertheless, the population figures of the entire countries were used, fully aware of an eventual distortion of the results. This method of presentation was chosen, since there are also other countries in which large sections of population

---

[3] Kolkka.

are debarred from Olympic representation, for social, political or racial reasons, though not divided by frontier lines.

Participation of China. China was represented at the Olympic Games with a team of the People's Republic of China. Since the acceptance of its participation by the International Olympic Committee was delayed, the team did not arrive in time, and took part in a very limited number of events. The participation and achievement results do not, therefore, give a true picture of the intended contribution of the Chinese to the Olympic Games.

COMPUTATION OF DATA

The Punch Card Method

In the processing of extensive statistical evidence considerable difficulties may be encountered. The amount of time and work which is required for its recording and computation is often excessive. Furthermore, there is always the risk of errors which is inherent in human performances. Also, there is the cost factor. The ingenious invention of Dr. Herman Hollerith has eliminated from statistical computation much of the human element. While preparing the Population Census Report of 1880 for the United States of America, Hollerith conceived the idea that in sorting the individual forms, the numerical information on each card could be recorded through punched holes. At first, he developed a device to sort cards mechanically. Later, it occurred to him that an electrically operated machine could be constructed to automatically sort the punched cards by allowing electrical impulses to enter a circuit which in turn selectively operates numerical counters. In some of the first punch card machines already each punched hole recorded a single unit, and different serial categories were selected in accordance with the varying positions of the holes in the card. Until today, punch card sorters operate on the same principle.

For example, if the year of birth of the individual is punched on the card as a two-digit number (*e.g.*, columns 8—9, see Fig. 1), the counter »3» for decimal figures (col. 8) senses a »unit count» direction from each card punched with an initial »3», *i.e.*, for all entries of year of birth from -30 to -39 (in the present study

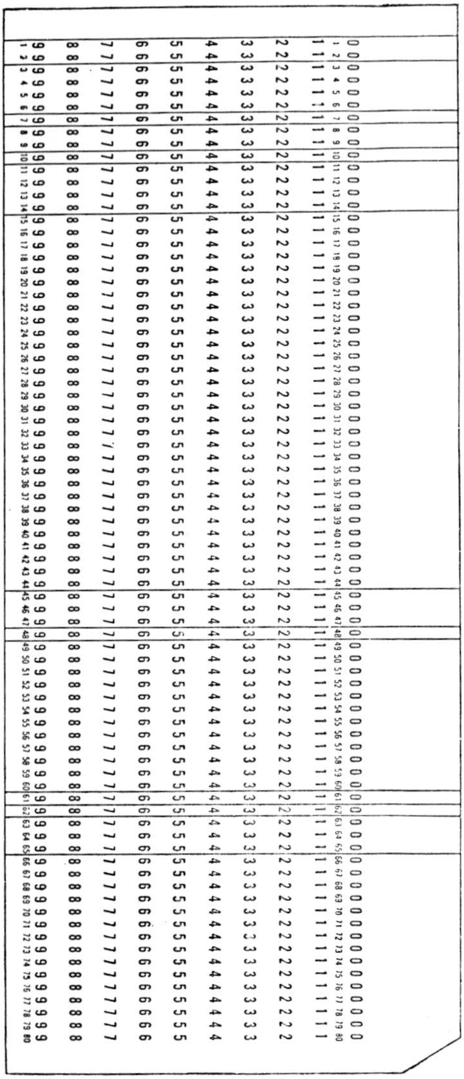

	INDIVIDUAL CARD	TEAM CARD
Punched entities:		
Code number of country		D:o
Initials of country		D:o
Sex *		Not in use
Year of birth		Not in use
Not in use		Not in use
Code number of sports event		D:o
Name of competitor		Not in use
Rank		D:o
Special code*		D:o
Result		D:o
Number of cards prepared		Not in use
Code number of race		Not in use
Points		D:o
Not in use		Not in use

Fig. 1. The punch card and the punching schedules of individual and team cards. Special code indicated with an asterisk was used for expressing information on disqualification, accident and other reasons for interruption of the competition.

1930—1939). The accumulated number of unit counts in this counter therefore indicates the total number of cards for persons born between 1930 and 1939.

Although the range of the first punch card machines was confined to the counting of cards, machines capable of adding or subtracting numerical information from punch cards have later been developed. Further, there are now available machines for multiplication and division, as well as electronic calculators with which computing operations of higher degrees of difficulties can be carried out. Alphabetic information can today be recorded on punch cards and re-interpreted on printed forms.

Since the time of its introduction the Hollerith punch card idea has grown into a highly differentiated system.[1] Though originally invented for statistical use, the system now is also applied to a multitude of other purposes in industry, business, public administration and in many scientific fields. The punch card method is extraordinarily flexible and suitable for a variety of purposes. It has greatly widened the field of application of statistical analysis.

The Punch Card. The punch card which was used in the present investigation is of standard dimensions, *i.e.*, it contains 80 columns (see Fig. 1), each of them subdivided into 12 vertical positions for holes to be punched. The uppermost two positions in each column are reserved for marking purposes, the other ten for recording of numerical entries from 0 to 9, in sequence from up to down. Each column or group of columns, also called »field», serves one specific purpose only. Hence, each category of information can be found in the same field on every card. For example, the year of birth for the Olympic athletes was punched into columns 8—9. Thus, the position of the hole in column 8 represents the tens of years in the two-digit age figure, while in column 9 the second digit is entered.

Entries on the Punch Card. Two types of cards were used in the present investigation, viz. *cards for individual competitors* and *cards for teams.* As to the former, single cards represented individual participation in an athletic event, provided such participation was recorded in the Olympic Bulletin. Thus, for

---

[1] Casey & Perry, 1951.

an athlete who participated in several events, several cards were punched, *i.e.*, one card for each event. As Emil Zatopek participated in the 5,000 m, 10,000 m and Marathon races, three separate cards were prepared for him. No separate cards were made for the elimination contests which were treated as parts of one and the same event. To give an example, one card only was prepared for each athlete participating in the 100 m race, even if he ran all three elimination heats and the final.

In computing the data for the team sports events, a card was prepared for each member of each team. In connection with the age analysis of this study, these individual cards for team members were included in the computations.

Separate cards were prepared for each team. The recording of information on punch cards for teams followed a pattern of its own. For example, the team has no age, though the members have. The difference between the recording of individual and team cards is shown in Figure 1.

Participation Assessment

In the subsequent analysis, the term *participation* will be used in reference to a distinct statistical unit. As stated before, for the individual athletic competitions each card records a *participation* in a single event; while for sportsmen who participated in several events, several cards were prepared. Similarly, in the case of the team sports events, each punch card represents one *team participation*. Individual cards were punched for each member of the teams, but these cards were used only for the age study and for athletes who also competed in individual events, *e.g.*, in gymnastics.

Point Allocation

A second statistical term to be defined is the *point value* of each participation. Points were allocated for each Olympic performance according to a novel method.

In an analysis which is concerned with the evaluation of different sports events like the Olympic Games, a common denominator is needed in order to render the results comparable. If all athletic achievements are to be »measured», it is necessary to express the results in accordance with an absolute scale. From the outset we asked ourselves: What is the »value» of a Gold Medal in boxing compared with the »value» of a Silver or Bronze Medal in the 10,000 m race? What is the combined »value» of these three medals? Such questions may be difficult to answer for a given individual case, but it is well worthwhile to answer them for the purpose of conducting a collective analysis of multiple sports events as is rendered possible by the availability of unique and numerically large samples which Olympic Games provide.

In track and field events, different point tables have been in use. For example, the International Amateur Athletic Federation has published tables for the evaluation of results in track and field events.[2] However, corresponding tables are not available for all sports events of the Olympic program, and certain athletic performances cannot easily be evaluated in an objective manner.

The rank, *i.e.*, the ordinal number allocated to every competitor, has at times been used as a basis of point allocation. A commonly applied method is to award 7 points for the first, and 5, 4, 3, 2 and 1 for the following places. An element of comparative equalization is thus introduced in that all winners obtain the same point allocation, irrespective of the nature of the event. However, there are drawbacks. For example, if there are six competitors only in an event, the one placed sixth obtains one point, though no effort may have been necessary to reach the sixth place; while in an event with 100 entries 94 will thus remain unassessed.

Considerations of this kind have led us to introduce a new point allocation system which was mathematically derived by Kihlberg.

Rank as Criterion of Point Allocation. Our system of point allocation is based on the rank of the competitor. The winner in each event is given 100 points, the one ranking last 0 points. The point »distance» between the winner and the one placed second, between the second and the third, *etc.*, depends on the total number of participants in the event: the larger the number of participants, the shorter the interval. Competition is likely to be harder

---

[2] Scoring Table for Men's Track and Field Events, 1952.

if there are many participants than if there are fewer entries. Also, in an event which is open to many participants, the difference in performance value will generally be smaller than in events contested by few competitors.

Point Allocation. In the case of many athletic events, the Olympic Bulletin gives complete ranking lists for all competitors. In such cases point allocation was made by means of tables which show the calculated value of any rank, depending on the number of participants in the event (see Table 5).

At times, however, the ranking in the Olympic Bulletin is incomplete. *E.g.,* for competitors who were eliminated in a heat, or disqualified, or who suffered an accident or were incapacitated for other reasons, different methods of evaluation had to be used. If a competitor was eliminated, *e.g.,* in a heat of a running event, he was allowed the point value calculated as against the total number of competitors who qualified for the next series of heats or for the final. If several competitors were thus eliminated, they all obtained at this stage equal point allocations. The same principle of evaluation was applied to athletes who were disqualified, injured, *etc., i.e.,* they were grouped together with those who were or could have been eliminated through heats, *etc.,* at the same stage.

A sample point allocation table is presented in Table 5. Figure 2 illustrates the interdependence between point allocation, rank and number of contestants according to the mathematical equations used by us.

The number of points thus allocated to the various countries in each sport are listed in Appendix 2 for the individual competitions, and in Appendix 3 for the team events.

Mathematical basis of the point allocation system. The following symbols will be used:

n = number of competitors in an event,

x = rank or the ordinal number of competitor, $x = 1,2,........n$,

$p = x/n$ = probability of achieving a rank equal to or better than x, *i.e.* the proportion of rank achievements equal to or better than x.

The mathematical basis of the point allocation system as de-

TABLE 5
EXAMPLE OF POINT ALLOCATION TABLES

Rank (x)	\ Number of Participants (n)																							
	2	3	4	5	6	7	8	9	10	11	12	13	14	15	16	17	18	19	20	21	22	23	24	25
1	100	100	100	100	100	100	100	100	100	100	100	100	100	100	100	100	100	100	100	100	100	100	100	100
2	0	37	50	57	61	64	67	68	70	71	72	73	74	74	75	75	76	76	77	77	78	78	78	78
3		0	21	32	39	44	47	50	52	54	56	57	58	59	60	61	62	63	63	64	64	65	65	66
4			0	14	23	29	33	37	40	42	44	46	47	49	50	51	52	53	54	54	55	56	56	57
5				0	10	17	24	27	30	33	35	37	39	41	42	43	44	45	46	47	48	49	49	50
6					0	8	14	18	22	25	28	30	32	34	35	37	38	39	40	41	42	43	44	44
7						0	6	11	15	19	22	24	26	28	30	31	33	34	35	36	37	38	39	40
8							0	5	10	13	16	19	21	23	25	27	28	29	30	32	33	34	34	35
9								0	5	8	12	14	17	19	21	22	24	25	27	28	29	30	31	32
10									0	4	7	10	13	15	17	19	20	22	23	24	25	27	27	28
11										0	3	6	9	11	13	15	17	19	20	21	22	24	24	26
12											0	3	6	8	10	12	14	16	17	18	20	21	22	23
13												0	3	5	7	9	11	13	14	16	17	19	19	20
14													0	3	5	7	9	10	12	13	15	16	17	18
15														0	2	4	6	8	10	11	12	14	15	16
16															0	2	4	6	7	9	10	12	13	14
17																0	2	4	5	7	8	10	11	12
18																	0	2	4	5	6	8	9	10
19																		0	2	3	5	6	7	9
20																			0	2	3	4	6	7
21																				0	1	3	4	5
22																					0	1	3	4
23																						0	1	3
24																							0	1
25																								0

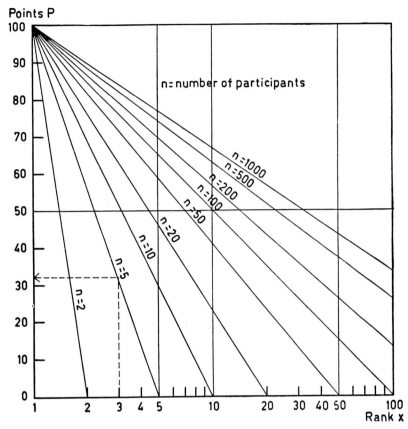

Fig. 2. Illustration of the point allocation system. For each possible number of participants (*n*), a separate line should be drawn, a sample of such lines being shown in the graph. The height of the vertical line drawn from any rank number *x* until crossing the appropriate *n*-line indicates the point value *P* of the rank in question. Example: five competitors (*n*=5); third man (*x*=3) receives 32 points (*P*=32).

scribed is derived from the statistical theory of information[3] which suggests that »the amount of information« carried by any probability event can be measured by means of the negative logarithm of the probability of the event. From this assumption, we have postulated that the rank *x* of the competitor in a sports event of *n* competitors, in proportion to the total number of competitors *n*,

---

[3] Barnard, 1951.

can serve as basis of an »information measurement», in that the negative logarithm of the »probability» of the x-th rank is taken as a measure of »information» on the relative importance of achieving that rank. Thus, the amount of information would be

$$-log\ p\ =\ -log\ \frac{x}{n}\ =\ log\ n\ -\ log\ x \qquad (1)$$

On the basis of the statistical theory of information, the quantity (1) would be a suitable common measure of different rank achievements. However, formula (1) implies that the top rank, that of the winner, will be allocated points exclusively according to the number of competitors. The larger this number, the higher the point allocation for the winner. But in case of combination of several different sports events it is not necessarily justified to grade the winners solely in accordance with the number of competitors in their respective events. On the contrary, it seems to be reasonable to allocate equal point values to all winners, irrespective of the event and of the number of participants. Such an allocation P can be achieved if the amount of information carried by the x-th rank, $-log\ p$, is expressed as a proportion of the maximum information for the entire event, *i.e.*, as a proportion of the information carried by the first rank, thus:

$$\begin{aligned} P\ &=\ -log\ p/- log\ \frac{I}{n} \\ &=\ (log\ n\ -\ log\ x)\ /log\ n \\ &=\ I\ -\ log\ x/log\ n. \end{aligned} \qquad (2)$$

Point values obtained by the formula (2), multiplied by 100, were used in this study. The winner thus is always credited with 100 points, the competitor placed last with 0 points. Formula (2) implies that, given the number n of competitors, the point allocation can be expressed as a linear function of the logarithm of the rank x of any competitor. In a graph where the vertical axis shows point values and the horizontal axis the logarithm of the rank, this function is simply represented by the straight line connecting the 100, 1 point with the 0, n point as shown in Figure 2.

Definition of Terms

The following terms are used in this study:
Participations: Number of participations from a country, *etc.*
Point share: Number of points collected by a country, *etc.*

Participation rate: Number of participations per million inhabitants.

Point rate: Number of points collected per million inhabitants.

Point level: Average number of points per participation.

Participations may be considered — with certain limitations — a measure of the active interest of a country in the Olympic movement. *Point share,* on the other hand, measures the country's success. *Participation rate* and *point rate* express the same things per unit of population. When the participation of a country rises close to the limit allowed, however, participation rate and point rate become lower than the athletic potential of a country might allow for. *Point level,* again, is a measure of the average quality of the participations.

In our tables the countries are listed—when not otherwise stated—in the order of decreasing point share.

The participations, point share, participation and point rates and point level of each country in the individual events are listed in Appendix 1. The point level of each country in team sports is shown in Appendix 4.

Statistical Methods

Tabulations were made and a number of statistical characteristics calculated in accordance with accepted principles of methodical procedure. In connection with the age analysis, *medians* were used instead of arithmetical means since computation work could thus be reduced. Also the median is less sensitive to extreme values than is the mean. The median or the *middle quartiles* divide the group under investigation into two sub-groups of equal size; so that in the age analysis the one-half of the members of the group are younger than the median age, the other half older. The term *average* will at times be used in referring to the median. As to the term *quartile:* the *first quartile* represents a point dividing the total sample in such a manner that one fourth of the individuals of the group are younger and three fourths older. The *third quartile* represents a point dividing the total sample in such a manner that one quarter of the individuals of the group are older and three fourths younger. The three quartiles thus divide the sample into four sub-groups of equal size.

For descriptive and analytic purposes a number of graphs were prepared. In most of the graphs the location of the countries participating in the Olympic Games is shown on a two-dimensional network by means of dots. In most, both the vertical and the horizontal axes are logarithmically subdivided, and the moduli of both the vertical and the horizontal axes are equal. This has the advantage over arithmetic subdivision that the unit of measurement does not affect the slope of the regression lines and the graphs are directly comparable. The slope of the regression lines superimposed upon the scatter diagrams expresses the relative effect of the »explanatory« variables upon the variables under investigation (in most graphs upon the number of points per million inhabitants). The steeper the line, the more pronounced the effect, *i.e.*, a relatively small change in the »explanatory« variable corresponds to a relatively large change of the variable under investigation.

In order to illustrate the general shape of the scatter diagram, the outermost dots have been connected with straight lines. The names of the countries belonging to such border lines are indicated in the figures.

Regression analysis. If there is correlation between the variables illustrated by means of scatter diagrams, the dots will form a relatively close cluster, clearly elongated in one direction or another. One can easily imagine a straight line as an axis through such a cluster in its elongated direction, this axis or line describing in a way the average tendency to dependence between the variables in question. For purposes of our analysis, mathematical equations of such lines, known as *regression lines*, have been determined by means of the method of least squares, widely applied in statistics. In general, the regression equation has the form

(3) $y = \text{constant} + b \cdot x$,

where we denote: $y = $ »dependent« variable, usually plotted along the vertical axis,

$x = $ »independent« or »explanatory« variable, usually plotted along the horizontal axis,

$b = $ regression coefficient, indicating the average »response« or increment in value of y per unit increment in value of x.

The larger b, the more sensitive the dependent variable y is on small changes in the explanatory variable x. In our analysis the units of measurement generally do not matter, for all the calculations have been performed using logarithms of the original numerical observations; hence, the slope of the regression lines (b being indicator of the slope) directly reveals the *relative* sensitivity of y on x. In other words, the steeper the regression line, the more sensitive the interdependence under investigation.

WORLD GEOGRAPHY AND WORLD POPULATION

Russia, USA, the Scandinavian Countries, Western Europe, Oceania and Middle and South America

The data were computed for the 8 geographical regions shown in Figure 3, *i.e.*, for North America, Middle America, South America, Europe, USSR, Africa, Asia and Oceania. Table 6 and Figure 4 reveal a number of relevant facts. The two leading athletic countries, *i.e.*, USA and USSR, do not dominate the global picture if their contributions are assessed in relation to their populations. Per million inhabitants, North America, that is USA and Canada, collected 65 points, as against 45 points collected by the USSR. These figures have to be judged in the light of the fact that the athletic representatives of Europe as a combined population—a block of about 400 million people—collected 124 points per million inhabitants. Oceania, *i.e.*, Australia and New Zealand, collected 200 points. The last figure, remarkable as it is, comes from a comparatively small population sample (13 millions) which for statistical reasons alone cannot be directly compared with much larger samples such as those for Europe (396 millions) and Asia (1 272 millions). Though athletic performance standards in Australia and New Zealand are high, the presence in the 1952 Australian and New Zealand teams of such extraordinary woman athletes as Miss Jackson, Miss Strickland and Miss Williams heavily tipped the scale for these two countries.

The athletic supremacy of Europe is established beyond any doubt. The athletic strength of the United States and of Russia is, at least to a degree, a reflection of the size of the population samples, from which these two large countries are able to choose their teams. If confronted with European blocks of comparative size the apparent superiority of the »Big Two» is no longer in evidence, as Table 6 demonstrates. However, the number of performances for Europe is 2 038, as against 239 for North America and 209 for USSR, *i.e.*, the large countries »compete» in this computation with smaller teams. This fact will have to be kept in mind.

We have calculated the combined Olympic point share of USSR and USA, *i.e.*, of a population sample of 346 millions, and compared that with the Olympic point share of the 4 Scandinavian countries, *i.e.*, Finland, Sweden, Denmark and Norway, with a combined population of 19 millions. USSR and USA collected 17 706 points, the Scandinavian countries 12 873 points. Per million population, the USSR + USA teams thus had 51 points to their credit, as against 678 points for the Scandinavian countries. The latter therefore »win» by 1 230 per cent. The total number of participations of the combined USSR and USA teams was 403, as against 483 for the combined Scandinavian teams. Thus the difference between the point rates is of very great significance, and cannot by any means be explained as a statistical artifact. The Scandinavian »victory» would be still greater if the results of the Winter Games had been included in the computation.

The point rates are of interest. The 44 points per million inhabitants for Middle America compare well with the 45 for USSR, especially if it is realized that these successes were achieved with 131 participations as compared to 209 participations of the Russians. South America's 40 points per million inhabitants were collected in 239 participations.

Africa

The comparatively low point rate — 17 — for Africa calls for comment. We have presented in Tables 2 and 3 and in Appendix I the number of participations and the point share of Egypt and South Africa. The teams of neither of these two countries contained black athletes. And in interpreting the African situation we are, in this context, interested primarily in the fascinating

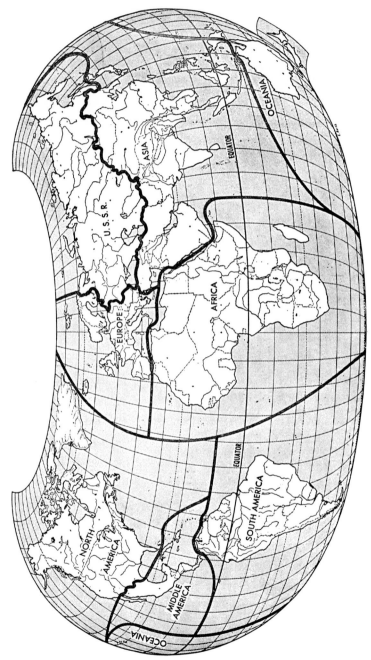

Fig. 3. Continents and regions of the world.
Woytinsky & Woytinsky 1953, p. 6.

physiological and social problems arising from the interplay between the extraordinary natural endowment which the black races possess for certain athletic events, and the environmental and political forces which modify these inherent abilities.

The true point rate for the »Africa of the Black Man», *i.e.* the territories south of the Sahara, is not much higher than that for Asia. But the total picture, as far as athletic achievements of the black athletes at the Olympic Games are concerned, is such as to suggest that this situation is somehow artificial. Though the vast majority of African blacks, for reasons of nutritional, epidemiological, administrative, educational and other shortcomings*), are not yet ready to send participants to Olympic Games, the remarkable contributions of black athletes from other parts of the globe, mainly from the United States and Jamaica, but also from Brazil and Cuba (Table 7), characterize the black races, at least for certain performance categories, as the most efficient of the three major racial groups of mankind, *i.e.* compared with the yellow-brown and the white groups. The average point level of

TABLE 6

OLYMPIC PARTICIPATION AND ACHIEVEMENT OF CONTINENTS AND REGIONS

Continents and Regions	Population in Millions	Partici- pations	Partici- pation Rate	Point Share	Point Rate	Point Level
North America	166	289	1.74	10 722	64.6	37.1
Middle America	51	131	2.57	2 269	44.5	17.3
South America	111	239	2.15	4 437	40.0	18.6
Europe	396	2 038	5.15	49 293	124.5	24.2
USSR	193	209	1.08	8 690	45.0	41.6
Africa	198	145	0.73	3 331	16.8	23.0
Asia	1 272	290	0.23	5 977	4.7	20.6
Oceania	13	86	6.62	2 601	200.1	30.2
Total	2 400	3 427	1.43	87 320	36.4	25.5

* According to a statement issued by the World Health Organization in 1951,[1] the ratio of physicians to population is 1:956 in Europe; 1:946 in North America, 1:2 505 in South America, 1:4 898 in the Middle East, 1:6 804 in Asia and 1:9 111 in Africa.
  [1] Chronicle of the WHO 1955, p. 212.

PARTICIPATION RATE

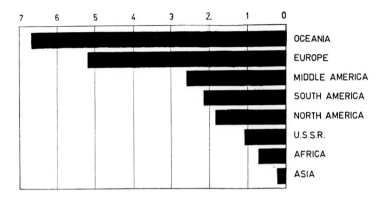

POINT RATE

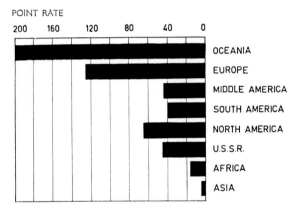

POINT LEVEL

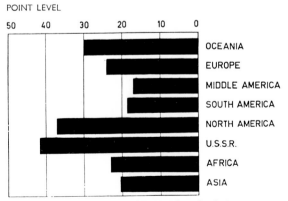

Fig. 4. Participation rate, point rate, and point level of the continents
and regions.

TABLE 7

THE REPRESENTATIVES OF THE BLACK RACE WHO QUALIFIED AMONG THE SIX
BEST. INDIVIDUAL COMPETITIONS

Sport	*Event*	*Rank*	*Country*	*Athlete*
Boxing	51 kg	1.	United States	Brooks
	63.5 kg	1.	United States	Adkins
	71 kg	semi-final	Argentina	Herrera
	75 kg	1.	United States	Patterson
	81 kg	1.	United States	Lee
	over 81 kg	1.	United States	Sanders
Weight-lifting	60 kg	3.	Trinidad	Wilkes
	90 kg	3.	Trinidad	Kilgour
	over 90 kg	1.	United States	Davis
		2.	United States	Bradford
Track and field, men	100 m	2.	Jamaica	McKenley
		3.	Great Britain	McDonald Bailey
	200 m	1.	United States	Stanfield
		3.	United States	Gathers
		4.	Great Britain	McDonald Bailey
		5.	Jamaica	Laing
	400 m	1.	Jamaica	Rhoden
		2.	Jamaica	McKenley
		3.	United States	Matson
		5.	Jamaica	Wint
	800 m	2.	Jamaica	Wint
	1500 m	5.	France	El Mabrouk
	110 m	1.	United States	Dillard
	Long jump	1.	United States	Biffle
		2.	United States	Gourdine
		4.	Brazil	Facanha de Sa
	High jump	3.	Brazil	Telles de Conceicao
	Hop, step and jump	1.	Brazil	Ferreira da Silva
	Decathlon	2.	United States	Campbell
Track and field, ladies	100 m	6.	United States	Faggs

Table 7 cont.   Team competitions

Sport	Event	Rank	Country	Athlete
Basketball		6.	Brazil	Monteiro Carvalho, Dos Santos
Track and field, men	4×100 m relay	1.	United States	Dillard, Stanfield
		4.	Great Britain	McDonald Bailey
	4×400 m relay	1.	Jamaica	Wint, Laing, McKenley, Rhoden
		2.	United States	Matson
Track and field, ladies	4×100 m relay	1.	United States	Faggs, Jones, Hardy

the black race was as high as 37.3, against 25.0 of the white race and 26.6 of the yellow-brown race.

A few African blacks were included at the 1952 Olympic Games in the teams from Nigeria and Gold Coast, *i.e.*, territories under the British Crown enjoying a degree of political and civic independence which at that time was not conceded to other colonial societies in Africa. In the British and French national teams were a few African negroes, though several black athletes in the British and French teams came from territories outside Africa.

Africa harbours a great athletic reserve army which has not yet been fully mobilized for the Olympic contests. Its 180 million black people, Negro, Bantu and Hamitic, as well as other anthropological entities, such as the numerically small nation of the Watussi in Ruanda-Urundi who are known to be outstanding high jumpers,[2] are bound to play an increasingly important role in the Olympic Games in the future, as their educational, health and civic development continues.

For centuries the enormous volume of physical ability that is potentially available in Africa, was held back by poverty and malnutrition, by superstition and lack of education. But with the

---

[2] Jokl, 1941.

progressive industrialization of Africa, with the development of political consciousness of the African people, there is no doubt that more and more physical forces will be released and cultivated, with the result that African athletes will eventually play a major role at the Olympic Games. The handful of American (10% of the total population of the USA are coloured) and West Indian negroes whose exceptional natural abilities have been allowed to develop in the political climate of the democratic American and British societies, have by their athletic achievements presented an impressive contrast to the substandard picture which black man's Africa as a whole offered until recently. The challenge to France, Belgium, Portugal, Spain and South Africa, *i.e.*, the major European powers to whom the future of the African black people was entrusted, was obvious already in 1952. Similar considerations apply to the self-governing African countries such as Egypt, Libya, the Sudan and Ethiopia, and to the United Nations Trust Territories of Tanganyika, Cameroon, Togo, South West Africa and Ruanda-Urundi. The political developments in the decade following the 1952 Olympic Games corroborated the validity of these considerations.

Asia

As a result of the political situation in 1952, the People's Republic of China was not represented at the Games. However, the significance of the singularly low point rate for Asia per million inhabitants (4.7) is not thus invalidated. The vast population complex of Asia, numbering at the time about 1 300 million people, is—in terms of physical fitness and efficiency—even behind the black man's African continent south of the Sahara desert.

Inherently, the yellow-brown populations possess considerable physical abilities, an observation which is of crucial importance since it supports the conclusion that on the whole the athletic backwardness of the Asiatic block is of environmental origin. The success of the Japanese track and field, gymnastic, free style wrestling and swimming contestants, of the Indian field hockey players, of the yellow-brown members of the American swimming team; of Korea in boxing, weight-lifting and the Marathon race, of the Philippines in the weight-lifting and boxing contests (Table

TABLE 8

THE REPRESENTATIVES OF THE YELLOW-BROWN RACE WHO QUALIFIED AMONG
THE SIX BEST. INDIVIDUAL COMPETITIONS

Sport	Event	Rank	Country	Athlete
Boxing	54 kg	semi-final	Korea	Kang
Free style wrestling	52 kg	2.	Japan	Kitano
	57 kg	1.	Japan	Ishii
	62 kg	5.	Japan	Tominaga
	67 kg	6.	Japan	Shimotori
	73 kg	5.	Japan	Yamazaki
Weight-lifting	56 kg	4.	Korea	Kim, H.
		6.	Philippines	Landero
	60 kg	4.	Philippines	Del Rosario
		6.	Singapore	Chay
	67.5 kg	1.	United States	Kono
		4.	Korea	Kim, G.
	75 kg	3.	Korea	Kim, S.
Swimming, men	100 m free style	2.	Japan	Suzuki
		4.	Japan	Goto
	400 m free style	2.	United States	Konno
	1500 m free style	1.	United States	Konno
		2.	Japan	Hashizume
		3.	Brazil	Okamoto
		6.	Japan	Kitamura
	100 m back stroke	1.	United States	Oyakkawa
Swimming, ladies	400 m free style	3.	United States	Kawamoto
Gymnastics, men	Floor	2.	Japan	Uesako
		4.	Japan	Ono
	Rings	6.	Japan	Takemoto
	Long horse	2.	Japan	Takemoto
		3.	Japan	Ono
		3.	Japan	Uesako
Track and field, men	Marathon	4.	Korea	Choi
	Pole vault	6.	Japan	Sawada
Track and field, ladies	Discus	4.	Japan	Yoshino

Table 8 cont'd   Team competitions

Sport	Event	Rank	Country	Athlete
Swimming, men	4×200 m relay	1.	United States	Konno
		2.	Japan	Suzuki, Tanigawa, Hamaguchi, Goto
Swimming, ladies	4×100 m relay	3.	United States	Kawamoto
Gymnastics		5.	Japan	Ono, Uesako, Takemoto, Kaneko, Nabeya

8) and the other achievements of representatives of the racial group under discussion which are summarized in Tables 9 and 10, are therefore of special significance. With the rapid social and political evolution of the people of Asia, as is now in progress, there will be in evidence in the near future an increasingly noticeable rate of participation and of success of Asiatic populations in Olympic competitions.

OLYMPIC COMPETITIONS FOR WOMEN

Athletic Achievements

Of the 69 countries which were represented at the 1952 Olympic Games, 27 did not send any woman competitors. Among them were Turkey, Greece, Ireland and Spain; Egypt, Nigeria and Gold Coast; Pakistan, the Philippines, Iran, Indonesia, Ceylon and Viet-Nam. Considering that the countries listed in Table 1 were not represented at Helsinki at all, the total population of the regions from which no women came to the Games amounted to 1,100 millions.

India with its 350 million people entered 7 woman athletes; Israel with its 1 million, 4; neither Egypt nor Jordan nor Syria nor Yemen nor Iraq delegated any female participants; South

TABLE 9
THE POINT SHARE OF EACH RACE IN INDIVIDUAL COMPETITIONS

Sport	Point Share				Per Cent Distribution of Points			
	White	Yellow-Brown	Black	Total	White	Yellow-Brown	Black	Total
Shooting	7 273	31	.	7 304	100	—	.	100
Canoeing, men	1 790	.	.	1 790	100	.	.	100
Canoeing, ladies	424	.	.	424	100	.	.	100
Fencing, men	4 613	19	.	4 632	100	—	.	100
Fencing, ladies	955	.	.	955	100	.	.	100
Modern pentathlon	1 209	.	.	1 209	100	.	.	100
Boxing	6 141	276	835	7 252	85	4	11	100
Free style wrestling	3 998	313	.	4 311	93	7	.	100
Greco-Roman wrestling	3 822	.	.	3 822	100	.	.	100
Weight-lifting	3 377	386	300	4 063	83	10	7	100
Cycling	2 564	7	13	2 584	99	—	1	100
Equestrian	3 335	7	.	3 342	100	—	.	100
Rowing	538	.	.	538	100	.	.	100
Swimming, men	6 218	1 159	.	7 377	84	16	.	100
Swimming, ladies	4 219	206	.	4 425	95	5	.	100
Gymnastics, men	3 211	222	.	3 433	94	6	.	100
Gymnastics, ladies	2 666	.	.	2 666	100	.	.	100
Athletics, men	18 259	450	2 355	21 064	87	2	11	100
Athletics, ladies	5 795	116	330	6 241	93	2	5	100
Total, men	66 348	2 870	3 478	72 696	91	4	5	100
Total, ladies	14 059	322	330	14 711	96	2	2	100
Total	80 407	3 192	3 808	87 407	92	4	4	100

TABLE 10
THE PERCENTAGE CONTRIBUTION OF EACH RACE IN WORLD POPULATION, IN
TOTAL NUMBER OF PARTICIPATIONS AND IN POINT SHARE

Subject	Per Cent Distribution			Total
	White	Yellow-Brown	Black	
World population	56.4	34.0	9.6	100.0
Participations	93.5	3.5	3.0	100.0
Point share	92.0	3.7	4.3	100.0

Africa's team of 9 women was restricted to members of the white race; British-governed Hong Kong sent 3 women. On the whole, the United States, Europe, Russia and the British Dominions displayed by far the greatest interest in the women's events at the Olympic Games.

Table 11 lists the number of participations and point share, and also indicates the point level of each country for the two sexes separately. Complementary to Table 11 is Table 12 which facilitates a comparison of the contribution of each country's man and woman athletes in the Games. The first column indicates the ratio of women's participation to the summed participations of men and women. In the next column this ratio is expressed as percentage of the mean ratio. A country with an average participation ratio of women is allocated the figure 100, countries with more than average participation of women rank higher than 100, and *vice versa.* The next two columns express the sex distribution of the point share computed analogously. The Netherlands—a country governed by a succession of queens—revealingly shows the highest ratios for women, both in terms of participation figures and of point share. The last column shows the ratio of women's and men's point levels. According to this figure, the female athletes of New Zealand were the world's best as compared to their male compatriots, with a ratio as high as 2.27.

A global analysis of the data for participation and athletic achievements at the Olympic Games reflects the social status of women in the different countries. The nations which were conspicuous by their absence from the Olympic Games, or who did not include women in their teams, generally are distinguished also by unfavourable, or by comparatively unfavourable conditions, in respect of child mortality, rates of morbidity and mortality, as well as longevity. Conversely, the high participation and athletic success ratios for the United States, the USSR, Europe and the British Dominions reflect social advancements, at least of those population groups from which the teams were selected.

A special problem arises from the Olympic analysis which is of relevance for the general practice and theory of physical education and which has also a bearing on our general concept of the woman's position in society. If on a global scale a high standard

Medical Sociology of Sport

TABLE 11

<small>Participations, Point Share, and Point Level of Men and Women, by
Country. Individual Competitions. The Countries Are Listed
in the Order of Total Points</small>

Country	Partici-pations of Men	Partici-pations of Women	Point Share of Men	Point Share of Women	Point Level of Men	Point Level of Women
1. United States....	155	39	7 725	1 291	49.8	33.1
2. USSR..........	163	46	6 475	2 215	39.7	48.2
3. Sweden........	127	24	4 795	458	37.8	19.1
4. Hungary.......	95	30	3 386	1 340	35.6	44.7
5. Germany......	106	33	3 399	1 087	32.1	32.9
6. Finland........	147	32	4 004	432	27.2	13.5
7. Great Britain...	135	45	3 373	1 019	25.0	22.6
8. France........	135	34	3 238	620	24.0	18.2
9. Italy..........	102	21	3 106	504	30.5	24.0
10. Czechoslovakia..	59	12	1 963	423	33.3	35.3
11. Australia.......	60	14	1 490	682	24.8	48.7
12. Switzerland.....	93	12	1 878	84	20.2	7.0
13. South Africa....	47	9	1 384	494	29.4	54.9
14. Argentina.......	64	14	1 615	199	25.2	14.2
15. Japan..........	50	13	1 592	199	31.8	15.3
16. Denmark.......	59	15	1 233	431	20.9	28.7
17. Canada........	66	17	1 386	261	20.3	15.4
18. Netherlands.....	28	31	685	888	24.5	28.6
19. Romania........	63	13	1 347	183	21.4	14.1
20. Norway........	74	5	1 495	27	20.2	5.4
21. Poland.........	62	22	1 135	342	18.3	15.5
22. Belgium........	70	4	1 266	81	18.1	20.3
23. Brazil..........	53	8	1 153	133	21.8	16.6
24. Egypt..........	73	.	1 258	.	17.2	.
25. Austria........	47	21	804	402	17.1	19.1
26. Mexico.........	47	4	868	26	18.5	8.7
27. Iran...........	22	.	849	.	38.6	.
28. Yugoslavia......	43	10	711	121	16.5	12.1
29. Turkey.........	31	.	755	.	24.4	.
30. Bulgaria........	26	10	432	227	16.6	22.7
31. India..........	30	7	490	63	16.3	9.0
32. Jamaica........	9	3	519	23	57.7	7.7
33. Chile..........	32	3	496	39	15.5	13.0
34. Luxembourg.....	31	.	506	.	16.3	.
35. Portugal........	44	3	493	6	11.2	2.0

Country	Partici- pations of Men	Partici- pations of Women	Point Share of Men	Point Share of Women	Point Level of Men	Point Level of Women
36. Venezuela.......	43	2	475	10	11.0	5.0
37. Korea..........	14	1	442	5	31.6	5.0
38. New Zealand....	8	4	201	228	25.1	57.0
39. Spain..........	17	—	359	.	21.1	.
40. Cuba..........	20	—	342	.	17.1	.
41. Ireland........	21	—	338	.	16.1	.
42. Greece........	25	—	301	.	12.0	.
43. Philippines.....	15	—	296	.	19.7	.
44. Guatemala.....	26	2	237	18	9.1	9.0
45. Lebanon.......	9	—	255	.	28.3	.
46. Saar...........	25	3	226	29	9.0	9.7
47. Pakistan.......	28	—	252	.	9.0	.
48. Puerto Rico.....	21	—	236	.	11.2	.
49. Israel.........	15	4	165	17	11.0	4.3
50. Uruguay.......	15	1	160	22	10.7	22.0
51. Nigeria........	11	—	146	.	13.3	.
52 Trinidad.......	3	—	127	.	42.3	.
53. Iceland........	14	—	120	.	8.6	.
54. Hong Kong.....	6	3	86	31	14.3	10.3
55. Bermuda.......	8	4	79	33	9.9	8.3
56. Singapore......	5	2	87	18	17.4	9.0
57. Thailand.......	12	—	100	.	8.3	.
58. Burma........	5	—	74	.	14.8	.
59. Ceylon........	6	—	69	.	11.5	.
60. Indonesia......	3	—	57	.	19.0	.
61. Gold Coast.....	5	—	49	.	9.8	.
62. Monaco.......	8	—	39	.	4.9	.
63. Viet-Nam......	7	—	38	.	5.4	.
64. Liechtenstein....	2	—	17	.	8.5	.
65. China.........	1	—	11	.	11.0	.
66. British Guiana..	1	—	8	.	8.0	.
67. Panama.......	1	—	—	.	—	.
Total..........	2 848	580	72 696	14 711	25.5	25.4

TABLE 12
COMPARISON BY COUNTRY OF WOMEN'S AND MEN'S PARTICIPATION, POINT SHARE, AND POINT LEVEL

Column 1: Sex ratio in participation (= women's participations per cent of total participations).
Column 2: Sex ratio in participation, per cent of average sex ratio.
Column 3: Sex ratio in point share (= women's point share per cent of total point share).
Column 4: Sex ratio in point share, per cent of average sex ratio.
Column 5: Women's point level per cent of men's point level.

FOR FURTHER EXPLANATION, SEE PAGE 75

Country	1	2	3	4	5	Country	1	2	3	4	5
United States	20	119	14	85	67	Venezuela	4	26	2	13	46
USSR	22	130	26	152	121	Korea	7	40	1	7	16
Sweden	16	94	9	52	51	New Zealand	33	197	53	316	227
Hungary	24	142	29	170	126	Spain	—	—	.	.	.
Germany	23	140	24	144	103	Cuba	—	—	.	.	.
Finland	18	106	10	58	50	Ireland	—	—	.	.	.
Great Britain	25	148	23	138	90	Greece	—	—	.	.	.
France	20	119	16	96	76	Philippines	—	—	.	.	.
Italy	17	101	14	83	79	Guatemala	7	42	7	42	100
Czechoslovakia	17	100	18	105	106	Lebanon	—	—	.	.	.
Australia	19	112	31	187	196	Saar	11	63	11	68	108
Switzerland	11	67	4	26	35	Pakistan	—	—	.	.	.
South Africa	16	95	26	157	187	Puerto Rica	—	—	.	.	.
Argentina	18	106	11	65	56	Israel	21	125	9	55	39
Japan	20	120	11	66	48	Uruguay	6	37	12	72	206
Denmark	20	120	26	154	137	Nigeria	—	—	.	.	.
Canada	21	121	16	94	76	Trinidad	—	—	.	.	.
Netherlands	53	311	57	336	123	Iceland	—	—	.	.	.
Rumania	17	101	12	71	66	Hong Kong	33	197	27	158	72
Norway	6	37	2	11	27	Bermuda	33	197	29	175	84
Poland	26	154	23	138	85	Singapore	29	169	17	102	52
Belgium	5	32	6	36	112	Thailand	—	—	.	.	.
Brazil	13	78	10	61	76	Burma	—	—	.	.	.
Egypt	—	—	.	.	.	Ceylon	—	—	.	.	.
Austria	31	183	19	110	112	Indonesia	—	—	.	.	.
Mexico	6	36	3	17	47	Gold Coast	—	—	.	.	.
Iran	—	—	.	.	.	Monaco	—	—	.	.	.
Yugoslavia	19	111	15	86	73	Viet-Nam	—	—	.	.	.
Turkey	—	—	.	.	.	Liechtenstein	—	—	.	.	.
Bulgaria	28	164	34	205	137	China	—	—	.	.	.
India	19	112	11	68	55	British Guiana	—	—	.	.	.
Jamaica	25	148	4	25	13	Panama	—	—	.	.	.
Chile	9	50	7	43	84						
Luxembourg	—	—	.	.	.						
Portugal	6	38	1	7	18	Averages	17	100	17	100	100

of physical efficiency of women forms an integral part of a superior pattern of health and of growth and of fitness of the societies concerned, a re-examination would appear to be overdue of the traditional reserve with which the subject of physical activities and of physical training for women is still today treated by the majority of educationists and of physicians, a reserve which is projected into the general attitude towards women of our time. de Beauvoir's[1] conclusion seems to be corroborated by our data, viz. that the contemporary social status of women, even in the »progressive« countries, is characterized by restrictive influences of historical or even of pre-historical prejudices and taboos. Such physiological and clinical data as have become available during the past decades from scientific studies of women's athletics point towards the conclusion that biologically the female sex is more robust and more capable of adapting itself to the demands of environmental challenges than has so far been assumed.

This statement will be illustrated in three ways. First, certain conclusions will be drawn from the extremely high performance standards that were attained in the various Olympic contests for women. Secondly, a number of physiological and clinical data will be summarized which also support de Beauvoir's point of view. And thirdly, it will be shown that the aesthetic result of the development of women's athletics has been altogether satisfactory.

In the track and field events for women there were encountered not only outstanding individual feats but also an impressively broad level of high physical efficiency of the participants. 11 women ran the 100 meters in 12 seconds or faster. The times of the 6 finalists were 11.5, 11.8, 11.9, 11.9, 12.0 and 12.1. Miss Jackson ran the 200 meter race in 23.4, but the 6th in the final still clocked 24.6, and Miss Faggs failed to qualify for the final though she ran 24.5 secs in the VIth heat. Three girls ran the 80 meter hurdles in under 11 seconds, and 24 of the 33 participants in this event ran under 12 seconds. With one exception, all the 14 relay teams ran the 4×100 meter in under 50 seconds, with USA and Germany attaining 45.9 seconds. In the long jump, the 22nd

---

[1] de Beauvoir, 1953.

competitor still leaped 5.33 m, and the first two 6.24 and 6.14.
15 girls jumped 1.50 m high and more, the first three crossing the
bar at 1.67 m and 1.65 m and 1.63 m. Four girls put the shot more
than 14 m, the winner having a throw of 15.28 to her credit. 11
girls threw the discus more than 40 meters, the winner 51.42 m.
15 girls hurled the javelin more than 40 meters, the first two more
than 50 meters.

The results of the other competitions for women at the Games
confirmed the impression that *a new type of woman is evolving
as a result of the physical education and sports movement of this
century.* The traditional concept of the universal physical inferi-
ority of the female sex does no longer hold good as a categorical
assumption. Adaptive resources of the female sex which in the
past were expended in order to resist nutritional, climatic and
other primitive strains have, under the influence of social and
technological advancements, become available for new uses.

In studies of the growth of physical efficiency in children,[2] it
has been demonstrated that among physically untrained children
the muscular performances of a large sector of the best girls equal
or surpass those of a great number of the less efficient boys. This
performance potential of girls can be greatly developed through
systematic training, training being effective on every individual,
irrespective of initial performance levels.

Now, what is so remarkable in the growth of physical efficiency
as it is revealed in the Olympic analysis is the twofold phenome-
non that the majority of women throughout the world are un-
affected by this progressive trend of increasing physical efficiency
while many among those women who *are* thus affected attain
standards of performance which are far above those of the average young healthy male population, even in the most advanced
societies. It is a common practice to compare athletic record
performances of men and women and of commenting on the
differences which are thus apparent. But such an approach leads
to a fallacious picture. The vast majority of healthy males, young
ones as well as older ones, are physically untrained and would
have no chance to compete with success against physically well

---

[2] Jokl, 1946.

trained women, even if we were to disregard the exceptional athletic performance standards of the Olympic woman competitors. A track and field team consisting of Mesdames Jackson, Hasenjager, Strickland, Brouwer, Blankers-Koen, Golubichnaja, Sander, Williams, Chudina, Cawley, Brand, Lerwill, Zybina, Romaschkova, Bagrjanceva, Dumbadze, Zatopkova and Gorschakova would in 1952 have beaten the majority of all boys' High School and University teams throughout the world.

What we are witnessing at present are the physiological effects of a new dynamic concept which the athletic movement has introduced and which on an increasing scale alters the phaenotype of mankind, of a concept which mobilizes biological forces that have been lying dormant for millennia. This statement applies to men as well as to women though in the case of the latter to a much greater degree, for the reasons which de Beauvoir has so impressively stated in her great book.

We have compared the results in the track and field competitions for men at the first Olympic Games in Athens in 1896 as well as subsequently, with the 1952 performances of the women. At the 1896 Olympic Games, T. E. Burke won the 100 meter race for men in 12 seconds while Miss Jackson won the 100 m race in 1952 at Helsinki in 11.5, with Miss Hasenjager coming 2nd with 11.8, followed by Mesdames Strickland and Cripps, both being timed 11.9. E. H. Clark of the United States won the broad jump for men at Athens in 1896 with 6.35 m as against the jump by Miss Williams of 6.24 m with which she won the same event in 1952 in Helsinki. In May 1956, Miss Thelma Hopkins broke the women's world high jump record by clearing 174 cm; at the 1906 Games, the men's high jump was won with 177.5 cm. Mr. R. S. Garrett's winning discus throw of 29.15 m in Athens in 1896 is far below the 51.42 in Finland in 1952 by Miss Romaschkova of USSR, and the shot put of Mr. Garrett of 11.22 m at Athens in 1896 is below the 15.28 m of Miss Zybina of USSR at Helsinki 1952, even if it is taken into account that the women use somewhat lighter weights. At the end of 1955 the world record in shot put for women was 16.29 m and for discus 57.04 m. At the 1896 Games in Athens, Hache of Hungary won the men's 100 meter free style swimming race in 1 min. 22.2 secs, while at the

1952 Games in Helsinki Miss K. Szoke, also of Hungary, came first in the women's 100 meter free style race in 1 min. 06.8 secs. Miss V. Gyange of Hungary won the women's 400 meter free style swimming competition at Helsinki in 1952 in 5 mins. 12.1. The extraordinary class of this performance falls into perspective if it is recalled that Mr. C. M. Daniels of the USA won the same race for men at the 1904 Games at St. Louis in 6 min. 16.2 secs., that Mr. O. Scheff of Austria won the event at the 1906 Olympic Games in 6 mins. 23.8, that Mr. H. Taylor of Great Britain won the Gold Medal for the same event in 1908 at the London Olympic Games in 5 min. 36.8, that Mr. G. R. Hodgson of Canada did likewise at the 1912 Games in Stockholm in 5 min. 24.4, and Mr. N. Ross of the USA captured the race in 1920 at the Antwerp Olympic Games in 5 min. 26.8. In 1922 Johnny Weissmuller established his famous free style swimming world record over 400 meters of 5 min. 06.6—but Miss Hveger of Denmark has swum a time of 5.00.1 thus creating a new world record for women with which she would easily have beaten the American champion in his record race 34 years ago.

Physiological and Clinical Data

The second argument supporting the assertion that the female sex is more robust and more capable of adapting itself to the demands of environmental challenges than has so far been assumed, is of a physiological and clinical kind.

Exercise, even in its competitive forms, does not disturb the normal menstrual cycles of trained athletes. On the other hand, even a number of athletic records have been established during menstruation.[3, 4]

It has at times been asserted that female athletes have a narrow pelvis. Actual examinations give no basis for such assertions. The skeletal measurements of former champion athletes have shown no departure from normal dimensions.[5]

---

[3] Kral & Markalous, 1937.
[4] Ingman, 1953.
[5] Niemineva, 1953.

The data on the fertility rates and deliveries of outstanding woman athletes or former woman athletes are all normal. The course of delivery leaves no doubt that the functional state of the pelvic and peritoneal muscles is excellent.[5, 6]

The fact that all physiological and obstetrical data as obtained from female athletes are normal also answers two questions that have been frequently raised, namely, whether track and field activities, such as the broad and the high jump, may cause damage to the pelvic organs; and whether performances of endurance such as the half mile race overtax the resources of the cardiovascular system of women. Both questions can be answered in the negative.

Physiologically, the woman is fully capable of active participation in the sports movement.

Age, Fitness and Social Status

Currently, the age span of participation of women athletes in top level competitions increases. Young girls of 15, 14, and even 13 have attained Olympic honours. Until 25 years ago it was unusual to encounter married women among champion performers. A process of acceleration of growth and of deceleration of ageing characterizes the growth pattern of our time. A large number of the Olympic finalists in the women's events of the 1952 Olympic Games were married and had children. Many of them were over 35 and at least two were grandmothers.

The old belief that women age earlier than men seems to be fallacious. In 7 out of 18 Olympic competitions in 1952 in which the performance data for men and women were directly comparable, the oldest female competitors were older than were the oldest men competitors (Table 13, Figs. 5 to 8). In four instances the average age of the female competitors was slightly higher than were the corresponding age figures for the men, though the opposite statement applies in 15 other events. In most athletic competitions the youngest women were between 14 and 16 years old—though they were beaten in many instances by competitors

---

[6] Pfeifer, 1951.

15—20 years older. One of the ancient dreams of womankind, namely that of retaining their youth, has been brought nearer to fulfilment.

It is only about fifty years ago that women began to claim their right to participate in sports and games and athletics. For a long time their efforts encountered considerable resistance. They were told that sports would produce »a masculine type of woman»; that »exercise makes girls muscle-bound»; that participation in competitive athletes »would lead to difficulties in childbirth»; even rare developmental malformations were alleged to be caused through athletic training.

In the meantime, millions of girls have indulged in sports, gymnastics and games; competed in swimming, in track and field events and on horseback; women have climbed some of the highest mountains and swum through a thousand rivers and lakes. They have derived therefrom some of the most valuable experiences of their lives. All the evil ghosts of whom they had been warned have remained conspicuous by their absence. That the present generation of women grows stronger; that their maturation is balanced; that the state of health of young mothers and of their children today is superior; that 30 year old women no longer look old; that many school girls now play and exercise in the same teams as their mothers; and, as the gymnastic mass display of housewives at the 1949 Lingiad at Stockholm demonstrated, even with their grandmothers; all this is, at least in part, the result of the intense interest they are taking in physical activities. Sports and games and athletics for women are significant elements of what is best in contemporary culture, women are about to shake off civic disabilities which millennia of prejudice and ignorance had imposed upon them.

Prejudicial views are still widely held about women's exercise. The degree of rejection of these superstitions is reflected in the participation and success of women's representatives from the various regions of the world.

Aesthetic Criteria

A third criterion for the evaluation of women's athletics is an aesthetic one. Parallel with the growth of athletic performance standards there has taken place during the past 50 years or so a display of new dynamic patterns of motion and form which contain elements of artistic value and of creative beauty. The great woman hurdlers and discus throwers, fencers and divers, gymnasts and canoeists have introduced—unwittingly, of course— features of elegance and of power, of force and of competence such as had previously not been known. That sports and athletics should be able to elicit in women categorical values of this kind and that performance and beauty should thus be correlated is a surprising and highly relevant experience.

AGE AND ATHLETIC PERFORMANCE

»There is no age limit for competitors in the Olympic Games.»

OLYMPIC RULES, § 40

The analysis of the distribution of the ages of the participants in the various competitive events revealed a difference of more than 50 years between the ages of the youngest and the oldest participants. Boys and girls of 13 and 14, women of 45 and men of 66 took part in the Games (Table 13).

Distinct age patterns were noted for the participants in the different athletic contests. *E.g.,* the average age of the men who took part in the swimming events was 21.5 as against an average age of 37 for the competitors in the shooting competitions. Average ages under 25 were found also for the cyclists, boxers and runners (100—1 500 m), 110 and 400 m hurdlers and jumpers, average ages of over 30 for the participants in the shooting events, for the horse riders, fencers, walkers and Marathon runners. Average ages of between 25 and 30 were found in the decathlon men, drivers, oarsmen, free style wrestlers, canoeists, 5 000 m runners, Greco-Roman wrestlers, 3 000 m steeplechase runners, throwers, weight lifters, pentathlon competitors and 10 000 m runners (Fig. 5).

In the running events, the average age of the competitors shows a marked progressive increase with the distance above 1 500 metres. Is endurance in running associated with middle age rather than youth? In cycling, the average age of the participants of the 190.4 km road race—which requires more than five hours'

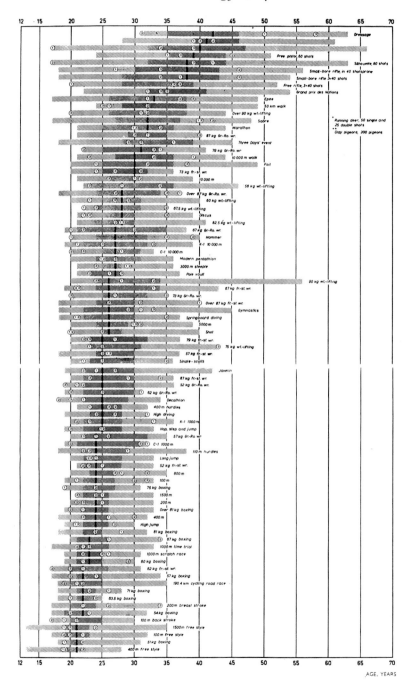

AGE, YEARS

effort—was as low as 22 years. Similarly, in swimming the 1 500 m free style race which is definitely an endurance event, the winner was timed 18 min. 30.0 sec. Nevertheless the average age of the participants was only 21 years. In running 5 000 metres which takes somewhat less time than swimming 1 500 metres, the average age was five years higher, 26 years.

The average ages in the different sports and events are in general agreement with those previously described for Finnish sportsmen,[1] though minor differences exist.

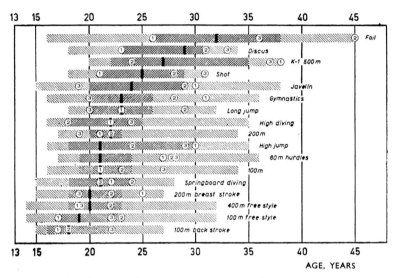

Fig. 6. Age distribution of participants in women's individual competitions. For symbols see Fig 5.

---

[1] Karvonen, 1955.

←

Fig. 5. Age distribution of participants in men's individual competitions. The thick vertical line shows the average age (= median, see p. 62). The age range is shown by the length of each horizontal column; the range between the first and third quartiles (see p. 62) is marked with thicker shading, that below the first and above the third quartile with thinner shading. The events are arranged in the order of the average ages.

TABLE 13
THE YOUNGEST AND OLDEST PARTICIPANTS OF THE OLYMPIC GAMES, 1952.
INDIVIDUAL COMPETITION

Event	Age	Rank	Name	Country
Men 17 years of age or younger.				
400 m free style swimming	13	Elim. in heats	E. Granados	Spain
1500 m free style swimming	13	Elim. in heats	E. Granados	Spain
Clay pigeons, 200 pigeons	17	1.	G. Genereux	Canada
Silhouette, 60 shots	17	2.	S. Kun	Hungary
Epee	17	Elim. in 1st round	H. Tonhat	Viet-Nam
Sabre	17	Elim. in 1st round	E. Lopez Ortega	Venezuela
1000 m time trial	17	26.	T. Kato	Japan
Free style wrestling 62 kg	17	2.	N. Guivechtchi	Iran
Boxing 57 kg	17	Elim. in 3rd round	E. Brown	United States
200 m breast stroke	17	Elim. in heats	K. Gleie	Denmark
"	17	Elim. in heats	M. Hashir	Pakistan
Boxing 54 kg	17	Elim. in 2nd round	H. von Graventiz	South Africa
100 m back stroke	17	2.	G. Bozon	France
"	17	Elim. in heats	T. Pettersen	Norway
100 m free style swimming	17	6.	R. Aubrey	Australia
400 m free style swimming	17	4.	P. Duncan	South Africa
"	17	Elim. in heats	P. Head	Great Britain
1500 m free style swimming	17	7.	P. Duncan	South Africa
"	17	Elim. in heats	S. Kelly dos Santos	Brazil
Men 60 years of age or older.				
Clay Pigeons, 200 pigeons	60	14.	E. Jenkins	Great Britain
"	60	5.	K. Huber	Finland
Running Deer. Number of shots 50 single and 25 double shots	61	11.	C. Braed	Great Britain
Dressage	63	18.	C. Jensen	Denmark
Silhouette, 60 shots	63	13.	E. Alava	Spain
Clay Pigeons, 200 pigeons	66	35.	C. Lucas	Great Britain
Ladies 15 years of age or younger.				
100 m free style swimming	14	Elim. in heats	G. Priestley	Canada
"	14	Elim. in heats	S. Miyabe	Japan
400 m free style swimming	14	Elim. in heats	G. Priestley	Canada
100 m back stroke	15	5.	B. Stark	United States
"	15	Elim. in heats	L. Fisher	Canada
"	15	Elim. in heats	M. Hunyadfi	Hungary
200 m breast stroke	15	Elim. in heats	E. Ward Petersen	Denmark
Springboard diving	15	5.	C. Welsh	Great Britain
Javelin	15	13.	M. Larney	United States

Event	Age	Rank	Name	Country
		Ladies 38 years of age or older.		
Javelin	38	16.	K. Parviainen	Finland
K—1 500 m	38	1.	S. Saimo	Finland
Foil	39	1st round	T. Mattsson	Finland
Foil	40	1st round	M. Kalka	Finland
Foil	40	1st round	V. Poulsen	Denmark
Foil	40	Semi-finals	E. Müller-Preis	Austria
Foil	42	2nd round	M. Elek	Hungary
Foil	44	1st round	K. Mahaut	Denmark
Foil	44	Semi-finals	G. Kunz	Austria
Foil	45	Semi-finals	F. Filz	Austria
Foil	45	2.	I. Elck	Hungary
		TEAM COMPETITIONS		
		Men 17 years of age or younger.		
Dragon Class	13	11.	W. Horton, Jr.	United States
Water-polo	13	8.	E. Granados	Spain
Pair-oars with cox	14	1.	B. Malivoire	France
Four-oars with cox	14	Elim. in heats	L. Omedes	Spain
5.5 m class	16	1.	M. Schoettle	United States
Four-oars with cox	16	Semi-finals	L. Andersen	Norway
"	16	Semi-finals	J. Arripee	Argentina
"	16	4.	L. Guest	Great Britain
Dragon Class	17	17.	A. Nelis	Belgium
Sabre	17	1st round	O. Lopez	Venezuela
Water-polo	17	1st round	J. Jones	Great Btirain
4000 m team pursuit race	17	12.	L. Serra	Uruguay
"	17	19.	T. Kato	Japan
"	17	20.	R. Echegaray	Venezuela
4×200 m relay swimming	17	7.	P. Duncan	South Africa
"	17	Elim. in heats	R. Aubrey	Australia
"	17	Elim. in heats	S. Kelly dos Santos	Brazil
		Men 60 years of age or older.		
Star Class	60	21.	V. de Sigaldi	Monaco
6 m R-Class	62	4.	S. Salen	Sweden
		Ladies 15 years of age or younger.		
4×100 m relay swimming	14	Elim. in heats	G. Priestley	Canada
"	15	Elim. in heats	L. Fisher	Canada
4×100 m relay	15	1.	B. Jones	United States
		Ladies 35 years of age or older.		
Gymnastics	35	1.	G. Urbanovitch	USSR
"	36	15.	M. Hoesly	United States

It is worth noting, that in some of the women's sports, top level performances were attained at an earlier age than in the corresponding men's events. Perhaps, women attain full maturity in athletic prowess at a younger age than men (Fig. 6). In some of the swimming events, the average of the participants was less than 20 years, and in all but one of the women's events girls under 20 took part. The results of the Olympic Games thus rather are in favour of early participation of women in competitive sports. As has been discussed on p. 82, medical and other evidence also warrant such recommendation.

Average ages are of limited significance. Of greater significance is the age range of the participants. In the fencing competitions the range of ages amounted to 3 decades, the youngest male fencer being 20 and the oldest 49, the youngest female fencer being 16 and the oldest 45. In canoeing for men the age range was 20—36, for women 20—38, in the swimming for men 13—45, for women 14—36, in apparatus gymnastics for men 15—45, for women 16—36, in the track and fields events for men 15—42, for women 18—38 (Figs. 5 and 6).

The age structure of the teams in the various team sports reflects the same general tendencies as seen in the individual events (Figs. 7 and 8). Again, wide age ranges exist. The inclusion of representatives of two generations in the same team may be looked upon as a positive cultural element, as it helps to channel some of the heritage of the senior members to the younger generation.

The white, black and yellow-brown races showed little difference in the age of their Olympic representatives. The Japanese and other yellow-brown swimmers were not younger than their white competitors, though such a belief has sometimes been expressed. The average age of the black runners was slightly higher than that of the white men at the same distances. This difference, however, did not reflect a slower maturation of the black, but was caused by the fact that some of the black runners had continued their running career for a longer time than the white sprinters and middle-distance men.

In all »progressive« countries of the world, the growth process of the present generation is distinguished by two features which

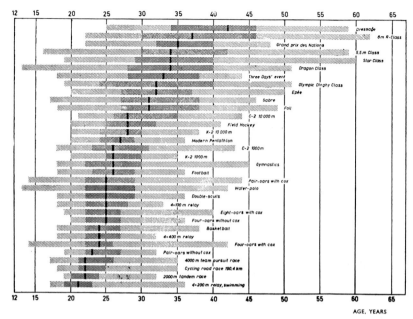

Fig. 7. Age distribution of participants in men's team competitions.
For symbols see Fig. 5.

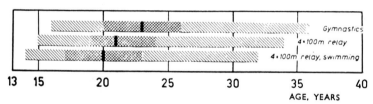

Fig. 8. Age distribution of participants in women's team competitions.
For symbols see Figure 7.

differentiate it from the growth pattern of past generations: by
an acceleration of growth and by a deceleration of ageing. Children today grow faster, mature earlier and attain larger dimensions than did children of past generations. A British high school
boy today is not likely to fit into a knight's armour in the Tower
of London. The clothing items worn in Lappland 200 years ago
which are exhibited in the Helsinki National Museum would be
too small for the present inhabitants of Lappland. German army
recruits in 1939 were taller and weighed more than did their

fathers when they were called to the colours in 1914. Today's
Russian boys and girls of 16 and 17 years of age cannot wear the
shoes and hats of their fathers and mothers. Men and women
marry earlier. The process of acceleration of growth and maturation is the result, mainly, of the conquest of the infectious diseases
and of the improvement of nutrition which has occurred during
the first half of this century.

At the same time, a radical biological change has taken place
in the later parts of life. Longevity is on the increase, largely due
to a decline of infant mortality. Mean life expectancy at birth was
about 50 years in the United States around 1900, and is now over
70. Men of 40 and 50 and 60 today are »younger» than were men
of 40 and 50 and 60 half a century ago, notwithstanding the fact
that there has been an increase during the period under review
of the degenerative diseases, especially of the circulatory system,
in this age range. Even during the past 30 years or so a remarkable change has taken place. A comparison of the results of the
athletic performances in the same events at the Alters-Turn-Fest
at Cologne in 1928, and at Marburg in 1952 indicated that in
1952 physical efficiency standards of 40—50 year old men were
superior at a rate suggesting a deceleration of the ageing process
during the period under review by 6—10 years.[2]

As Diem has shown,[3] the acceleration of growth is reflected in
an increasingly larger number of young boys and girls participating in international sporting events. The same statement can be
made for the older age groups. The results of the age analysis of
the Olympic data for 1952 supply corroborative evidence. The
age span of competitors at Olympic Games was 53 years; the
youngest participants were 13 and the oldest 66 years old; age
differences of over 20 years were in evidence in many competitions. On the basis of favourable endowment and good environment, physical training may render an adolescent boy or girl
maximally efficient physically and enable him to maintain a high
level of bodily fitness until near the end of his life. The 45 year
old Finnish gymnast Savolainen and the 42 year old German
gymnast Schwarzmann came 4th and 2nd respectively in the

---

[2] Jokl, 1954.
[3] Diem, 1952.

apparatus competitions at Helsinki; grandmothers participated with success in some of the athletic events for women. Participation in athletic activities of one kind or another is now possible almost throughout the whole length of life. This conclusion is supported by the description of several hundred gymnasts, male and female who competed in the Marburg Alters-Turn-Fest, with many of the men over 75, and many of the women over 55 years old.

Acceleration of growth and deceleration of ageing are correlated with the social and cultural advancement of the society.

Individual cases of middle age and old men or women with outstanding physical performance capacity have been known for a long time. What is new is that nowadays such cases become common, as the age distribution in the various Olympic events illustrates; and that even top level performances in athletics are now within the reach of men and women above 40 and 50 and 60.

High performance levels among middle age men are seen not only in sport but also in occupational work. In working competitions of Finnish lumberjacks—the occupation with the highest caloric expenditure known—men older than 40 have qualified to National Finals, and the mean age of the finalists has been as high as 33 years.[4]

The sports in which the highest average age levels of the competitors were computed obviously are the ones which are particularly well suited for inclusion in systematic long term physical training programs for the older groups. Among them are shooting and horse riding, fencing, walking and Marathon running. But the opposite conclusion is not or not necessarily warranted, namely that the sports in which low age averages prevailed at the Olympic Games are unsuitable for older subjects. For example in swimming the lowest average age was noted. But swimming is certainly a suitable activity for old people, and the same statement applies to apparatus gymnastics, to rowing and canoeing and weight-lifting. Apparently, from age averages of top level performers for a certain sport, no general conclusions can be drawn as regards its suitability for purposes of attaining basic physical fitness or for maintaining efficiency.

---

[4] Karvonen, 1955.

SIZE OF THE COUNTRY

In terms of the number of participants and of athletic success the United States and the Soviet Union were the two leading countries at the 1952 Olympic Games. Both are large countries with populations of about 150 and 190 million inhabitants respectively (figures quoted for 1952). Their apparent supremacy has often been ascribed by the public to the great number of people from which these two countries draw their athletes. But such an interpretation does not account for all the facts. There are very large countries which did not do very well at the 1952 Olympic Games, such as India with 360, Pakistan with 75 and Indonesia with 74 million inhabitants. Number of inhabitants and size alone do not guarantee a country's athletic achievements.

To judge from the athletic success at the 1952 Games several small countries ranged almost as high as the »big two«. Sweden, Hungary and Finland are examples. Similarly, numerical participation in the various competitions of the Games and size of population of a country showed little relationship, as shown in Figure 9.*

Also, the ability of a nation to collect points at the Games does not or not necessarily depend on the size of its population. Figure 10 shows the number of points collected by the different countries plotted against the size of their populations. The absence of a correlation between the number of participations (Fig. 9) or point share (Fig. 10) on the one hand, and size of the nation on the other reflects favourably upon the smallest states, such as Bermuda, Monaco, Liechtenstein, Luxembourg and Iceland. These countries top the list in terms of participation rate and point rate. On the same token the »big two«, USA and USSR, are delegated into rather insignificant positions. But such a statistical presentation hardly gives a true picture of the events at the Games. The large countries, like the United States and the Soviet Union are debarred by existing regulations to enter teams large enough to compete on a-man-per-million-population-basis with the »dwarf states«. Conversely, the same regulations allow high

---

* Abbreviations of names of countries used in this and subsequent graphs are explained in Appendix I, col. 2.

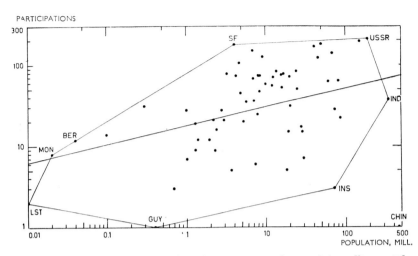

Fig. 9. Participation (*y*) as plotted against population (*x*) millions. The straight line represents the regression equation:

$$\log y \simeq \text{constant} + 0.24 \log x.$$

A weak positive correlation is observable.
China is left outside the envelope polygon, for reasons stated on p. 53.

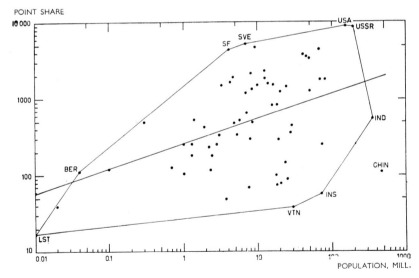

Fig. 10. Point share (*y*) as plotted against population (*x*) millions. The straight line represents the regression equation:

$$\log y \simeq \text{constant} + 0.33 \log x.$$

A tendency to a positive correlation can be observed.

TABLE 14
The Share of Countries of Different Size in the Olympic Participation
and Achievement
General Outlook

Size Groups	Total population in Millions	Partici- pations	Partici- pation Rate	Point Share	Point Rate
I. »Giant countries«; 150 millions and over	1 166	441	0.38	18 270	15.7
II. »Big countries«; 15 to 150 millions	820	1 316	1.60	30 627	37.3
III. »Medium size countries«; 1.5 to 15 millions	171	1 524	8.91	36 161	212
IV. »Small countries«; 150 000 to 1.5 millions	7.2	110	15.28	1 980	275
V. »Dwarf states«; less than 150 000	0.21	36	17.14	288	1 371

participation rates for the »dwarf states«. Their comparatively favourable success rating therefore does not necessarily reflect any outstanding achievements of their athletes.

Five Subdivisions. In order to remedy such artifacts, the countries have been listed in five groups, according to their population:

(1) »giant countries« with 150 million or more inhabitants;

(2) »big countries« with between 15 and 150 million inhabitants;

(3) »medium size countries« with between 1.5 and 15 million inhabitants;

(4) »small countries« with between 150 000 and 1.5 million inhabitants;

(5) »dwarf states« with less than 150 000 inhabitants.

The share of each of these five classes in terms of Olympic participation and success is sumarized in Table 14 and presented in detail in Table 15.

1 166 millions of the 2 500 million members of mankind live in the four »giant countries«; 820 millions in the »big countries« with 15—150 million inhabitants; and only less than 200 millions in the smaller states as listed under III, IV and V (Table 15). Nevertheless, in terms of the number of participants and of points collected in the Olympic competitions the »medium size countries«

of group III, *i.e.*, those with 1.5—15 million inhabitants each, were leading with 1 524 participations and 36 161 points. Their total population is only 171 millions. Quite close comes the group of »big countries» of group II, *i.e.*, those of between 15 and 150 million inhabitants, with a total population of 820 millions, 1 316 participations, and 30 627 points.

Dwarf States. Though the contribution of the dwarf states with less than 150 000 and that of the »small countries» with between 150 000 and 1.5 million inhabitants was numerically small, it still deserves attention. When the participation and point rates are examined (Table 14), the smallest countries rank very high, as was pointed out previously. This is an interesting result. Of course, these small countries had no chance to challenge the larger nations. But the very fact that in the true Olympic spirit they sent their athletes to the Games is noteworthy. For the small countries, sport is an effective and dignified means of cultural expression. At the Olympic Games they can present themselves on equal terms with economically and politically more powerful nations.

The Ancient Greek City States. It cannot have been a coincidence that the sports of the ancient world flourished in Greece, in a culturally homogeneous society consisting of numerous autonomous »city states». A comparable conceptual trend is noticeable in the modern Olympic Games: a common universal interest has been cultivated in that a large number of smaller and even of smallest units were integrated in a world-wide organization. The same general idea has been accepted by those responsible for the development of the sports movement in the British Commonwealth, as pointed out on page 40 and on page 42; the different members of the Commonwealth are competing in international sports as independent units. Similarly, the spiritual and cultural forces from 69 countries, large and small, merged into a powerful stream of common human experience at the Olympic Games.

General Smuts. General Smuts was the first to formulate philosophically the idea that the cultivation of the component parts of complex entities is a prerequisite for the evolution of vital as well as large social and political structures, like the British Com-

TABLE 15
THE SHARE OF COUNTRIES OF DIFFERENT SIZE IN THE OLYMPIC PARTICIPATION AND
ACHIEVEMENT (CF. TABLE 14)
Detailed Picture

Country	Population in Millions	Participations	Participation Rate	Point Share	Point Rate
I –Giant countries–					
United States	151.7	194	1.3	9 016	59.4
USSR	193.0	209	1.1	8 690	45.0
India	358.0	37	0.1	553	1.5
China	463.5	1	0.00	11	0.02
II.–Big countries–					
Argentina	17.2	78	4.5	1 814	105.5
Rumania	16.1	76	4.7	1 530	95.0
France	41.9	169	4.0	3 858	92.1
Great Britain	50.6	180	3.6	4 392	86.8
Italy	46.3	123	2.7	3 610	78.0
Germany	69.0	139	2.0	4 486	65.0
Egypt	20.4	73	3.6	1 258	61.7
Poland	25.0	84	3.4	1 477	59.1
Yugoslavia	16.3	53	3.8	832	51.0
Iran	18.8	22	1.2	849	45.2
Turkey	20.9	31	1.9	779	37.3
Mexico	25.4	50	2.0	894	35.2
Brazil	52.1	61	1.2	1 286	24.7
Japan	82.9	64	0.8	1 791	21.6
Korea	29.5	15	0.5	447	15.2
Philippines	19.6	15	0.8	296	14.9
Spain	28.3	17	0.6	359	12.7
Nigeria	24.0	11	0.5	146	6.1
Thailand	18.3	12	0.7	100	5.5
Burma	18.5	5	0.3	74	4.0
Pakistan	75.0	28	0.4	254	3.4
Viet-Nam	30.5	7	0.2	38	1.2
Indonesia	73.5	3	0.04	57	0.8
III –Medium size countries–					
Finland	4.1	179	43.5	4 436	1 082.0
Sweden	7.0	151	21.5	5 253	750.0
Hungary	9.3	125	13.4	4 702	505.6
Norway	3.3	79	24.0	1 522	461.2
Switzerland	4.7	105	22.5	1 962	417.4
Denmark	4.3	74	17.2	1 664	387.0
Australia	8.2	74	9.0	2 172	264.9
New Zeland	1.9	12	6.3	429	255.8

Detailed Picture

Country	Popula-tion in Millions	Partici-pations	Partici-pation Rate	Point Share	Point Rate
Czechoslovakia	12.6	71	5.6	2 386	189.4
Austria	7.1	68	9.5	1 206	169.9
Belgiumz	8.6	74	8.6	1 347	156.6
South Africa	12.3	56	4.6	1 878	152.7
Netherlands	10.1	59	5.9	1 537	152.2
Canada	13.8	83	6.0	1 600	115.9
Ireland	3.0	21	7.0	338	112.7
Puerto Rico	2.2	21	9.6	236	107.3
Venezuela	4.9	45	9.2	485	99.0
Chile	5.8	35	6.0	535	92.2
Bulgaria	7.2	36	5.0	659	91.5
Guatemala	2.8	28	10.0	255	91.1
Uruguay	2.4	16	6.7	182	75.8
Cuba	5.3	20	3.8	342	64.5
Portugal	8.5	47	5.5	499	58.7
HongKong	2.3	9	3.9	117	50.9
Greece	8.0	25	3.1	301	37.6
Gold Coast	3.7	5	1.4	49	13.2
Ceylon	7.5	6	0.8	69	9.2
IV –Small countries–					
Luxembourg	0.3	31	102.0	506	1 686.7
Jamaica	1.4	12	8.6	542	387.1
Saar	1.0	28	28.0	255	255.0
Lebanon	1.1	9	8.2	255	231.8
Trinidad	0.7	3	4.3	127	181.4
Israel	1.3	19	15.0	182	140.0
Singapore	1.0	7	7.0	105	105.0
British Guiana	0.4	1	2.5	8	20.0
V –Dwarf states–					
Bermuda	0.04	12	300.0	112	2 800
Monaco	0.02	8	400.0	39	1 950
Liechtenstein	0.01	2	200.0	17	1 700
Iceland	0.14	14	140.0	120	1 200

monwealth, the United States, the Federation of Soviet Repub-
lics, and, on a global basis, of the United nations.[1]

The results of our survey lend firm support to the view that the

[1] Smuts, 1926.

contemporary sports movement is a cultural force moving in the direction outlined by Smuts, for the emotional enrichment and the moral benefit of mankind.

Does Size of Country Determine Athletic Success? The claim has often been made that large countries have a better chance to find not only more but also better athletes among their populations than small nations. It is argued that athletic achievements depend very much on natural endowment, that physical gifts are distributed according to statistical laws and that there would thus be a better chance to find exceptional abilities—and combinations of abilities—in the large countries.

On the other hand, it may also be argued that success in Olympic contests is primarily due to training and to a smaller extent to innate individual abilities, in other words, that an average, normal person has a fair chance through systematic training to attain Olympic performance standards.

Testing a Hypothesis. If it were true that athletes coming from the big countries are better than those coming from small countries, it ought to be possible to demonstrate a correlation between the size of a country and the standards of the athletic performances of its representatives. The material at our disposal made it possible to test the validity of this hypothesis.

Figure 11 reveals a trend towards a higher point level at the Olympic Games as the size of the country increases. The grouping of the majority of countries is fairly close according to this trend. Trinidad and Jamaica deviate most in that these countries sent to the Games better athletes than the size of the country would have suggested—an observation explained in part at least by the singular endowment of their black athletes for certain competitive events, plus the social and economic opportunities afforded to the two islands under British rule. On the other side of the regression line are Viet-Nam, China, Pakistan, Thailand and India. The sports movement in these countries is young. Many of the participants were sent to the 1952 Games primarily to learn.

A closer examination of Figure 11 shows an interesting relationship. If a nation is ten times as numerous as another, it is—everything else being equal—likely to send a better athletes' team to

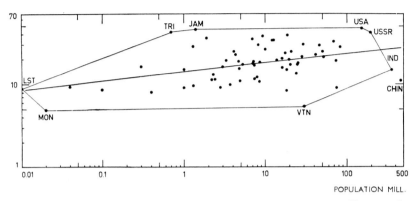

Fig. 11. Point level (y) as plotted against population (x), millions. The straight line expresses the regression equation:

$$\log y \quad \text{constant} + 0.11 \log x.$$

A weak tendency to a positive correlation can be observed.

the Olympic Games; but the athletes of the bigger nation will certainly not perform ten times as well as those of the smaller nation. In fact, the statistical prediction is that they will »win» by a margin of only 30 per cent. *In order for country B to build up a team of athletes who will collect twice the number of points per participation than country A, country B ought to have about 600 times more inhabitants!* This calculation is of course based on such statistical data as are available at this stage. The result of the computation would be rather different if the large Asiatic population block represented by India, China, Pakistan, Thailand and Viet-Nam would have been more advanced in 1952—as is likely to be the case in the future.

The empirical relationship described above is interesting and worth further studies. It has cultural, economic, industrial and military implications. If two countries of different size but with equally good manpower potential are comparable in quality of their manpower and material standards, the bigger nation of course starts with an advantage. But as the scatter of the athletic achievement points for the different countries indicates (Fig. 11), the size of a country is not the sole nor necessarily the prime determinator of the collective human efficiency pattern. The size of a country attains practical significance only when differences in the number of inhabitants are large.

CLIMATE

Rates of participation and achievement at the 1952 Olympic Games were unequally distributed for the different parts of the world. Since the physical and especially the climatic environment of man shows a great range of variation from the tropics to the circumpolar countries, the question arises as to the extent to which athletic efficiency is thus affected.

Temperature

The Olympic data were analyzed to examine the possibility of rates of participation and of athletic performances being determined by *temperature*. The accepted standard map of Annual Isotherm and Temperature Zones of the World (Fig. 12) was used as basis of evaluation. Each country was classified into temperature zones in accordance with the climato-geographic position of the region in which the majority of its population lives. Temperature zones »cold and cool», »cool and warm» and »warm and hot» of Table 16 include such countries in which the critical isotherms divide populated areas.

The results of the climatic analysis of the Olympic data are summarized in Table 16. The majority of the athletes who participated in the Olympic Games came from the three cooler temperature zones of the world. The three warmer zones were poorly represented, viz. by only about one sixth of the number of participations. The point rate of the warm zones was only one tenth of that of the cooler countries. *The 20° C or 68° annual isotherm proved to be collectively a dividing line for athletic achievement,* though attention will be drawn later on to highly significant exceptions from this statement. The distinctly favourable role played by the colder countries, as shown in the Olympic analysis, raises physiological questions of considerable relevance. Obviously, it is not the temperature factor as such which produces a high level of physical fitness and efficiency, but the adjustment

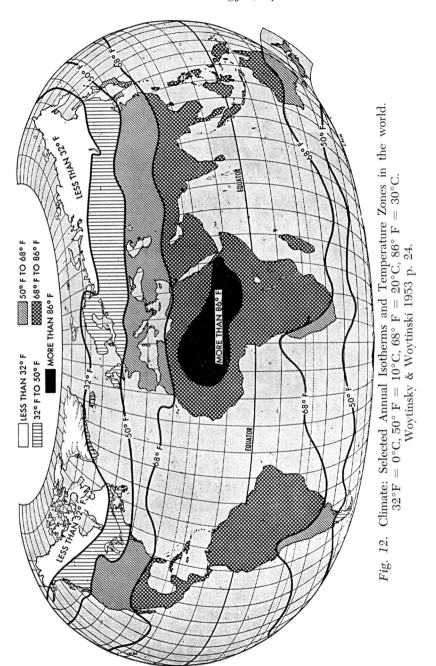

Fig. 12. Climate: Selected Annual Isotherms and Temperature Zones in the world.
32° F = 0°C, 50° F = 10°C, 68° F = 20°C, 86° F = 30°C.
Woytinsky & Woytinski 1953 p. 24.

to physical training in the colder countries takes place in a more effective manner. The average untrained inhabitant of the colder countries is, of course, not *eo ipso* superior athletically.

The extent to which individual countries fit into the general picture, is shown in Figure 13. The vertical scale indicates the point rate; the countries of the world are grouped in five blocks. Countries belonging in their entirety or partly to the zones on the colder side of the 20°C or 68°F Annual Isotherm, present a fairly homogeneous group. China seems to form the only exception, but as stated above, this result is a »political artifact» and does not reflect the athletic level attained or attainable in that country since China was not adequately represented at the 1952 Games.

Of particular interest are those countries on the hot side of the 20°C or 68°F Annual Isotherm whose athletes were successful at the Olympic Games. Though in absolute terms the number of outstanding athletes who come from the hottest temperature zones is small (Table 16), the fact that top level performers came at all from the hot regions of the world raises a significant physiological issue. Apparently, adaptation even to the hottest climatic environment can be so perfect that sufficient surplus energy becomes available for successful athletic training and competition

TABLE 16

OLYMPIC PARTICIPATION AND ACHIEVEMENT OF THE TEMPERATURE ZONES

Temperature Zones*	Population in Millions	Participations	Participation Rate	Point Share	Point Rate	Point Level
Cold...............	312	1 049	3.36	29 552	94.7	28.2
Cold & cool.........	246	417	1.70	14 979	60.9	35.9
Cool...............	401	1 395	3.48	32 472	81.0	23.3
Cool & warm.......	495	79	0.20	2 738	5.5	34.7
Warm.............	866	476	0.60	7 439	8.6	15.6
Warm & hot........	64	11	0.20	146	2.3	13.3

*Annual isotherms of temperature zones:
   Cold: 0°—10°C or 32°—50°F
   Cool: 10°—20°C or 50°—68°F
   Warm: 20°—30°C or 68°—86°F
   Hot: More than 30°C or 86°F

POINT RATE

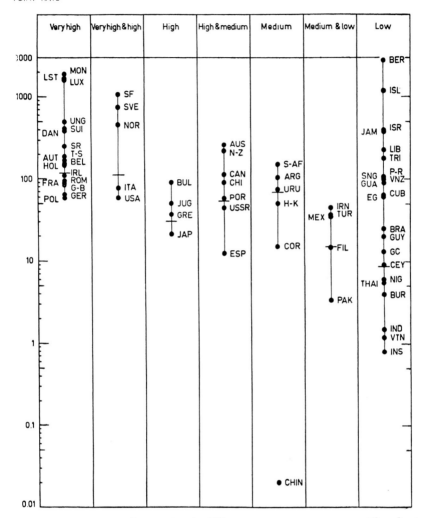

Fig. 13. Point rate of countries in different temperature zones. The short
horizontal lines represent the average point rate of each zone.

against subjects from regions in which climate does not impose
a comparative strain.

From Bermuda which lies in the 20—30°C or 68—86°F zone
came several good performers, but Bermuda is one of the »dwarf
states» and for this reason alone it is not directly comparable with

TABLE 17

LIST OF EVENTS IN WHICH ATHLETES COMING FROM COUNTRIES ON THE "HOT" SIDE OF THE 20° C OR 68° F ANNUAL ISOTHERM SUCCEEDED TO BE AMONG THE SIX BEST

Individual Competitions

Sport	Event	Rank	Country	Athlete
Free style wrestling	57 kg	3.	India	Jadav
	62 kg	4.	India	Mangave
Weight-lifting	56 kg	6.	Philippines	Landero
	60 kg	3.	Trinidad	Wilkes
		4.	Philippines	Del Rosario
	90 kg	3.	Trinidad	Kilgour
Equestrian	Grand prix des nations	4.	Brazil	Oliveria de Menezes
		6.	Mexico	Mariles
Swimming, men	1500 free style	3.	Brazil	Okamoto
	Springboard diving	4.	Mexico	Capilla, I.
		6.	Brazil	Busin
	High diving	2.	Mexico	Capilla, I.
		5.	Mexico	Capilla A.
		6.	Mexico	Perea
Track and field, men	100 m	2.	Jamaica	McKenley
	200 m	5.	Jamaica	Laing
	400 m	1.	Jamaica	Rhoden
		2.	Jamaica	McKenley
		5.	Jamiaca	Wint
	800 m	2.	Jamaica	Wint
	High Jump	3.	Brazil	Telles de Conceicao
	Long jump	4.	Brazil	Facanha de Sa
	Hop, step and jump	1.	Brazil	Ferreira da Silva
		3.	Venezuela	Devinish

the larger countries as discussed on p. 97. Nor can it be compared without qualification with all the other countries from the hot temperature zones. Similar considerations apply to Trinidad, Singapore and Hong Kong, all of which are very small countries. But there are also a number of larger countries in the hot zones with noteworthy athletic achievements; among them Puerto Rico,

Team Competitions

Sport	Event	Rank	Country
Basketball		3. 6.	Uruguay Brazil
Field hockey		1. 4.	India Pakistan
Yachting	Star class	4. 5.	Cuba Bahama
Equestrian	Grand prix des nations	4.	Brazil
Rowing	Double-sculls	3.	Uruguay
Track and field	4 × 800 m relay	1.	Jamaica

No woman athlete from this temperature zone qualified among the six best.

Venezuela, Guatemala, Uruguay, Cuba, Egypt, Jamaica, Mexico and Nigeria. Part of the latter lies in the hottest thermal zone of the world. All these countries produced and continue to produce evidence of significant athletic achievements as was shown at the British Empire Games in 1954 in which for the first time teams from Uganda, Tanganyika and Kenya participated.

Table 17 gives a list of athletes from countries on the hot side of the 20°C or 68°F Annual Isothem who were placed among the six best in their competitions. The total population of the countries from which those athletes came amounts to 560 mill., whereas the total population of other hot zone countries which were represented at the Olympic Games amounts to 210 mill. That part of the hot zone from which no teams at all were sent to Finland, covers a population of 800 mill., *i.e.,* more than 20 per cent of the population of the entire hot zone.

Although hot climate evidently represents a physiological handicap, it does not necessarily render the attainment of athletic success even at Olympic Games impossible. Some of the world's best runners came from Jamaica and the winners of the field

TABLE 18
"CLIMATIC ENERGY" AND OLYMPIC PARTICIPATION AND ACHIEVEMENT

Zones	Population in Millions	Participations	Participation Rate	Point Share	Point Rate	Point Level
Very high energy...	264	1 314	4.98	31 702	120.1	24.1
Very high and high energy...........	212	726	3.42	23 837	112.4	32.8
High energy........	116	178	1.53	3 583	30.9	20.1
High and medium energy...........	260	477	1.83	14 284	54.9	29.9
Medium energy.....	591	175	0.30	4 449	7.5	25.4
Medium and low energy...........	204	146	0.72	3 072	15.1	21.0
Low energy........	737	411	0.56	6 399	8.7	15.6

hockey tournament were Indians. Obiously, man—at least some men and women—can overcome the limitations imposed upon them even by the hottest climate on earth.

"Climatic Energy"

Temperature is not only the climatic factor of importance to man. Huntington has presented the concept of »*climatic energy*».[1] On the basis of studies of the efficiency of workers in different parts of the world under varying conditions of temperature and moisture, he has divided the world into four zones: of every high energy; of high energy; of medium energy; and of low energy (Fig. 14).

Does the analysis of athletic achievement level support Huntington's thesis? Table 18 indicates that the highest rate of athletic participation and of athletic point shares had on the whole to be allocated to the countries which are situated in the zone of »very high energy». Corresponding figures per unit of population are lower for the zones of lower energy. But no corresponding relationship was found when point levels were computed (Table 18, last column). Only for the zone of »low energy» was the

---

[1] Huntington, 1939, pp. 228-233.

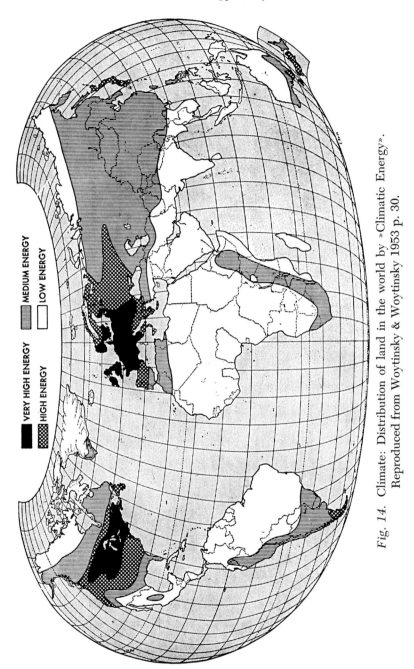

Fig. 14. Climate: Distribution of land in the world by »Climatic Energy«. Reproduced from Woytinsky & Woytinsky 1953 p. 30.

mean number of points per participation distinctly lower than for the other zones. Otherwise the impression was gained that some sort of All-or-Nothing law is operative in regard to athletics in that once an individual begins to excel physically his performance response to training is likely to continue favourably, almost irrespective of climatic environment.

In Figure 15 countries are grouped according to »climatic energy» zones, plotted against the point rate. In the zone of »low energy» a number of striking exceptions from the above described general rule were encountered. Bermuda, Iceland, Israel, Jamaica, Lebanon and Trinidad—all of them small countries— collected as many points per million inhabitants as did several countries in »better» climatic zones.

The large countries of the »low energy» zone—with the exception of Nigeria and Gold Coast—generally fell behind the athletic standards applicable to the »very high» and »high» energy zones.

Circumscribed areas within each climatic zone may have a climate which markedly differs from that of their surroundings. This consideration applies to Bermuda and Trinidad which are small ocean islands in the low energy zone, and to Lebanon, a mountainous country rising from a hot and dry plain.

Toynbee[4] sees in environmental limitations, climatic or other wise, potentially positive forces, challenges, to which a nation may succumb or, alternatively respond by mobilizing forces of survival in that they thus create cultures of their own. Israel, Jamaica and the Gold Coast are illustrations for such a possibility, each of them having succeded against different combinations of environmental difficulties, and each of them in turn evolving a different pattern of culture. If the stresses that are imposed upon a nation by an adverse environment are too great, or if the collective effort is too weak to produce and maintain a new culture, the society concerned will loose its identity, or even cease to exist. It has been said that too comfortable an environment may hamper cultural development. Though such a statement may be justified

---

[4] Toynbee, 1947.

POINT RATE

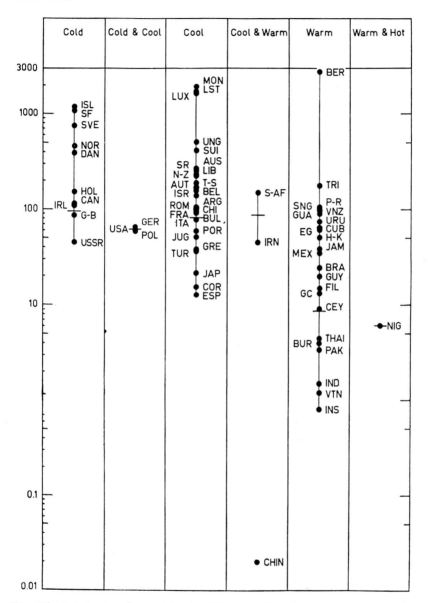

Fig. 15. Point rate of countries in different »climatic energy» zones: The short horizontal lines represent the average point rate of each zone.

in the light of historical evidence, the Olympic study has failed
to reveal supporting data for such an assertion.

Modern technology equips man with tools with which he can
change the climate in which he lives. Climatic handicaps have
been and will in future continue to be reduced, probably at a
rapidly increasing scale. That such developments will be reflected
in improved physical and athletic performance standards of the
people who reside in the hot and climatically »difficult» zones of
the world can not be doubted.

NUTRITION

> »*Das Volk, dessen Güte so sehr gepriesen wird, ist gar
> nicht so gut; es ist manchmal so böse wie einige andere
> Potentaten. Aber seine Bosheit kommt vom Hungern; wir
> müssen sorgen, dass das souveräne Volk immer zu essen
> habe; sobald allhöchst dasselbe gehörig gefüttert und gesät-
> tige sein mag, wird es Euch huldvoll und gnädig anlächeln,
> ganz wie die anderen.*»
>
> HEINRICH HEINE, 1852[1]

The nutrition of mankind shows wide variations. The amount
of food eaten varies from country to country, and also within each
nation depending on the social class and several other factors.
Similarly, different societies eat different kinds of food. The type
of the economy of the country, tradition and the wealth of the
individual are further important determinants of diet.

Energy Value of Food

The energy content of food eaten is expressed in kilocalories
(kcal.). A calory is a unit of energy. The law of the conservation
of energy renders it possible to establish a balance between the
amount of food eaten and the amount of energy expended. The
individual person who cannot afford to eat *ad libitum,* has in the
long run to restrict his activities. On the other hand, the only
way in which the body can react to eating more than it expends
is to pile up fat.

Comparative surveys of the amount of food eaten have been
made in many parts of the world. Global summaries have been

---

[1] Heine, Heinrich, 1852.

presented by Lord Boyd-Orr and subsequently by other experts of the United Nations' Food and Agricultural Organization. The number of calories per person is a mean figure established from studies of large population samples. It gives useful information on the nutritional situation of a country. A high caloric consumption tells that the majority of the population receives its vital caloric needs—and that its energy expenditure is therefore not in need of being restricted. However, noteworthy differences in caloric intake exist between nations which are sufficiently wealthy to satisfy their appetite. A striking relationship appears when participation and achievement in Olympic Games are evaluated against caloric consumption levels of the different nations.[2] Table 19 shows that the nations eating little are poorly represented. As the amount of food consumed increases, participation and number of points collected in the athletic contest rise concommitantly. Supporting this finding, the point level of individual athletes was the better, the higher the mean caloric consumption of their home countries. The discovery of such a relationship between caloric consumption and athletic achievement is one of the most important results of the survey. It reminds us of the intimate dependence of performance on the adequacy of the physiological mechanisms of the body.

When the focus is sharpened from the general picture to the individual countries, the same relationship holds. Fig. 17 shows the number of points per million inhabitants plotted against caloric consumption. The grouping of the countries indicates a clear cut correlation: The athletic achievement is the higher, the more energy is available from nutrition. That the point level varies much less than the number of points per million inhabitants had to be expected (Table 19). Competitors chosen to represent their countries at the Olympic Games are invariably in a physically satisfactory condition, nutritionally as well as otherwise, and once more we encounter the All-or-Nothing Law of athletic participation to which reference has been made before. A similar trend is in evidence also when individual countries are examined, as has been done in fig. 18. It shows the point level for

---

[2] Russell, 1954.

TABLE 19
OLYMPIC PARTICIPATION AND ACHIEVEMENT OF NATIONS ON DIFFERENT
LEVELS OF CALORIC CONSUMPTION

Kilocalories Per Head Per Day	Population in Millions	Participat- ions	Participat- ion Rate	Points	Point Rate	Point Level
1500—1999	432	40	0.09	610	1.4	15.3
2000—2499	749	397	0.53	8 709	11.6	21.9
2500—2999	82	264	3.24	5 936	72.7	22.5
3000—3499	232	969	4.17	29 324	126.1	30.3

each country plotted against caloric consumption. Thus, the nutritional status is reflected in the fact that the best nourished nations evidently can afford to send the greatest number of athletes to the Games, and vice versa; and that among individual participants in the Olympic contest those who came from the best fed countries are comparatively most successful.

The only countries falling out of the general grouping are Iceland and Ireland which are represented by rather small teams. Both these countries are distinguished by satisfactory standards of nutrition though this fact was not reflected in corresponding athletic achievements. But the size of the samples is too limited to allow any definite conclusion to be drawn.

Athletic achievement is closely connected with the average caloric consumption of the population. This statement is valid not only as a general tendency but also for individual countries. Obviously, nutrition is only one of many determinants of success in the Olympic Games, though probably quite a very significant one. *In order to produce good athletes, a nation must have an abundance of food, and in order to become a champion, a man or woman must be able to eat as much and as well as he or she likes.*

Quality of Food

In the training systems of athletes, the value of special diets has often been praised. Many athletes have been induced to eat food which contains unusually large amounts of meat or fruit or anything else in which trainer or trainee put their faith. Very

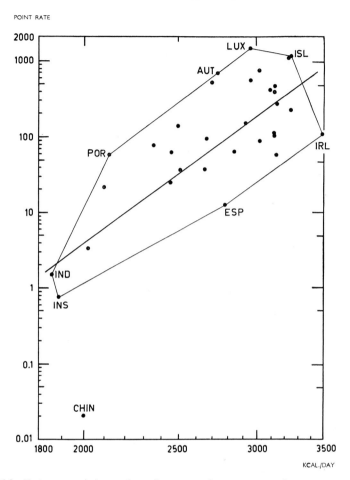

Fig. 16. Point rate (*y*) as plotted against the average caloric consumption per day (*x*). The straight line expresses the regression equation:

$$\log y \simeq \text{constant} + 9.47 \log x.$$

A definite positive correlation is observable.

little scientific evidence, however, has been adduced to support the claims of excellence of any such special nutritional regime, and none of the assertions under reference has found critical or scientific confirmations.

No detailed record was made of the eating habits of the individual Olympic athletes. We, therefore, can not make any state-

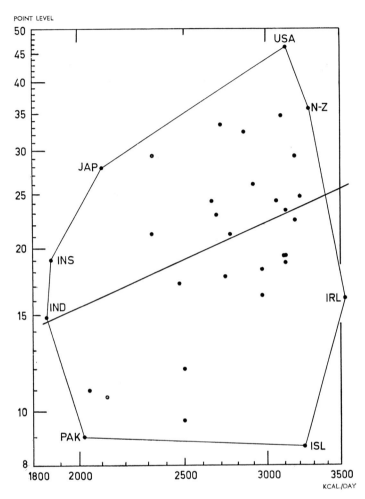

Fig. 17. Point level (y) as plotted against the average caloric consumption per day (x). The straight line expresses the regression equation:

$$\log y \simeq \text{constant} + 0.85 \log x.$$

Some tendency to a positive correlation is observable.

ment concerning the nutrition of each participant. However, information is available pertaining to the national dietary habits in the home countries of the competitors.[3]

The role of two nutrients, meat and sugar could thus be sub-

---

[3] Woytinsky & Woytinsky, p. 290.

jected to an analysis. The outcome was negative. The consumption of *meat*[3] seemed to have no relation whatsoever to athletic efficiency in so far as this factor could be tested in the present investigation. The Argentine, who consume the largest amounts of meat in the world, were neither better nor worse than the Rumanians who among the European nations eat least meat.

A corresponding study of the possible relations between athletic achievement and consumption of *sugar*[3] also yielded no conclusive answer. A sharp peak of participation rate and of point rate was observed in a group of countries which used 20—29 kg (40—59 metric pounds) sugar *per capita* per year: Ireland, Finland, the Netherlands, Belgium, Norway, and Chile. The nations consuming smaller amounts of sugar had on an average low participation and achievement figures. But, this result may be due to caloric restriction. Above the 29 kg per year level no definite correlation could be observed between sugar consumption and Olympic success.

Consumption figures for meat and sugar are to a large extent indicative of the standard of living in a country. At the same time, they fail to express social or economic factors on which athletic achievement depends.

Dietary Habits of Olympic Athletes

At the 1948 Olympic Games in London, the food eaten by a number of the participants was carefully studied[4]. A great variety was observed among the food habits of the subjects of the study.

At the Helsinki Games, the following experiences were gained in connection with catering for athletes.[5]

1. Consumption per head was high, 4,000-5,000 kcal. per day.
2. Diets differed during training and competing periods. Special care had to be paid to the quality and cooking of meat. In greatest demand were beef, mutton and chicken.
3. Foods fried in fat were avoided.

---

[4] Berry, Beveridge, Bransby, Chalmers, Needham, Magee, Townsend & Daubney 1949.

[5] Kolkka, p. 100.

TABLE 20
DEATH RATE AND OLYMPIC PARTICIPATION AND ACHIEVEMENT

Deaths per 1000 Inhabitants	Population in Millions	Participat- ions	Participat- ion Rate	Point Share	Point Rate	Point Level
5.0— 9.9	275	902	3.28	25 962	94.4	28.8
10.0—14.9	460	1 493	3.25	35 667	77.6	23.9
15.0—19.9	389	122	0.31	1 982	5.1	16.2
20.0—24.9	205	212	1.03	3 708	18.0	17.5

4. Little fish was eaten.
5: The most popular dessert was ice cream.
6. Wheat and graham bread were very popular.
7. The consumption of milk, butter, raw vegetables and fruit was heavy.
8. Honey, maltose and grape sugar played an important part in athletes' diets.
9. Canned raw foods were avoided.
10. Favoured beverages, along with milk, were ice water, fruit juices and mild pilsner.

VITAL STATISTICS

The extent to which the athletic representatives of a country succeed in Olympic Games can hardly be looked upon as a matter of pure chance. Common sense makes us presume that generally successful athletes come from nations which collectively possess a high performance capacity. The deleterious effects of disease on physical efficiency are well known. It therefore seemed likely that the athletic achievements of a country at the Olympic Games would somehow be related to its general standards of hygiene and health. The latter assumption can be gauged with the help of statistical data on longevity, morbidity and on mortality or death rates.

POINT RATE

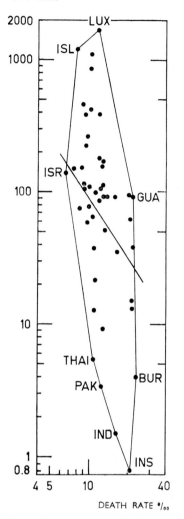

Fig. 18. Point rate (y) as plotted against death rate (x), pro mille. The straight line expresses the regression equation:

$$\log y \simeq \text{constant} - 1.50 \log x.$$

A negative correlation is observable.

Death Rates

The death rates[1] were related to the athletic achievement of the different countries in the Olympic contests in that point rate was relatively high for countries with a death rate below 15 deaths per 1,000 inhabitants, while the group of countries with higher death rates collected significantly fewer points per million inhabitants (Table 20). Moreover, in terms of point level the Olympic participants representing the latter group of countries were less successful than those coming from countries with low death rates, as shown by the last column of Table 20. The relationship between death rates and point rates for each country is shown in Figure 18.

Causes of Death. An analysis of the death rates according to causes revealed additional information. For example, the countries with the highest numbers of participations and points had proportionately high death rates from *cancer*[2]. This is, however, to be expected, since a decrease in the general death rate of the population is bound to lead to a proportional increase of individuals who live longer and who therefore are more likely to become afflicted with cancer. The predominant cause of death in people up to 30 years are the infectious diseases and in the underdeveloped countries this may be the largest age group in the mortality tables.

Between death rate from *tuberculosis*[3] and from *diseases of the heart*[4] of a country and its Olympic participation and success rate there was no definite relationship. The incidence of these two diseases seems to be but loosely correlated with those aspects of human culture and social organization which facilitate or determine athletic achievement.

Infant Mortality. Figures for infant mortality[5] showed a distinct relationship to athletic achievement. As can be seen from Table 21, the countries with the highest rates of infant mortality were the ones with the lowest rates of athletic success, and *vice*

---

[1] Woytinsky & Woytinsky, p. 163.
[2] Woytinsky & Woytinsky, p. 221.
[3] Woytinsky & Woytinsky, p. 212.
[4] Woytinsky & Woytinsky, p. 221.
[5] Woytinsky & Woytinsky, p. 169.

TABLE 21
INFANT MORTALITY AND OLYMPIC PARTICIPATION AND ACHIEVEMENT

Deaths per 1000 Live Births	Population in Millions	Participat- ions	Participat- ion Rate	Point Share	Point Rate	Point Level
25— 49	187	688	3.68	22 011	117.7	32.0
50— 74	160	621	3.88	15 564	97.2	25.1
75— 99	157	580	3.69	13 428	85.5	23.2
100—124	90	238	2.64	5 010	55.5	21.1
125—149	97	415	4.28	9 405	97.0	22.7
150—174	386	116	0.30	1 880	4.9	16.2
175—199	74	172	2.32	3 351	45.3	19.5
200—224	18	5	0.30	74	4.0	14.8

versa. In fact, statistical data pertaining to infant mortality are good indicators of the general state of health and fitness of the population concerned, and thus also of athletic efficiency.

There was a distinct correlation between Olympic success as measured by the number of points per million inhabitants and infant mortality (Fig. 19).

The close relation between infant mortality and athletic success rates became also apparent, when the average point levels were plotted against infant mortality rates for the different countries (Fig. 20). The most successful athletes generally came from the countries with the lowest infant mortality rates.

Evidently, infant mortality rate is a reliable indicator of cultural and social trends which also find expression in sports and athletics. More specifically, infant mortality seems to reflect most distinctly the incidence of all illnesses to which the children are subjected during the important years of their growth and development. Ratios used for measuring Olympic success are likely to be most favourable in members of societies whose children enjoy the greatest freedom from disease, from hunger and from want.

Birth Rates

The reported annual birth rates for countries taking part in the Olympic Games vary from 14.8 (Luxembourg 1950) to 48.7 (Guatemala 1950) per 1,000 inhabitants.[6] Birth rate of a country

[6] Woytinsky & Woytinsky, p. 140.

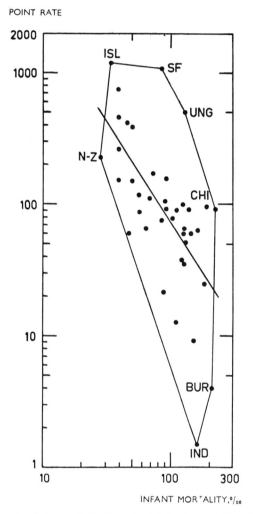

POINT RATE

Fig. 19. Point rate (y) as plotted against infant mortality (x), pro mille.
The straight line represents the regression equation:
$$\log y \simeq \text{constant} - 1.53 \log x.$$
A negative correlation is evident.

depends on a number of factors, many of which are well understood. Peculiarly, there is a definite correlation between birth
rate and infant mortality, in that nations with a high infant
mortality rate must have a high birth rate, to maintain their populations. Conversely, in countries with the lowest infant mortality

POINT LEVEL

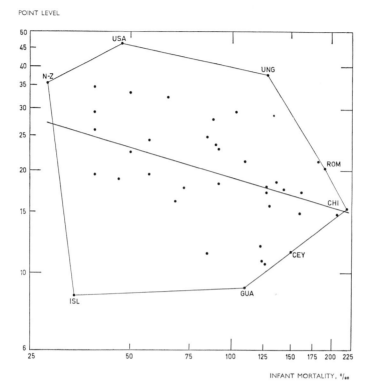

Fig. 20. Point level (y) as plotted against infant mortality (x) pro mille.
The straight line expresses the regression equation:
$$\log y \simeq \text{constant} - 0.29 \log x.$$
A tendency to a negative correlation is definitely observable.

rates—such as New Zealand, Iceland, Australia, Norway, the Netherlands, Sweden, Switzerland, United States, Denmark and England—birth rates for 1950 ranged from 16.1 to 24.6. On the other hand, countries with the highest infant mortality rates, among them Chile, Burma, Rumania, India, Ceylon, Colombia, Bulgaria, Costa Rica and Yugoslavia had a range of birth rates from 19.6 (Rumania) to as high as 46.5 (Costa Rica).

Economic factors are obviously important as are religious, psychological and other influences. Some authors have considered a low birth rate to be an indicator of lack of national vitality.

A correlation between birth rates and participation and point rates at the Olympic Games is shown in Table 22 which indicates

TABLE 22
BIRTH RATES AND OLYMPIC PARTICIPATION AND ACHIEVEMENT

Births per 1000 Inhabitants	Population in Millions	Participat- ions	Participat- ion Rate	Point Share	Point Rate	Point Level
10.0—19.9	330	1 270	3.85	32 793	99.4	25.8
20.0—29.9	836	1 236	1.48	33 606	40.2	27.2
30.0—39.9	108	160	1.48	2 393	22.2	15.0
40.0—49.9	505	137	0.27	1 819	3.6	13.3

that the participation rate was highest in the group of countries with the lowest birth rates, and that the same ratios decreased, as birth rates increased. The same applies, even more distinctly, if the point rate is taken as criterion of evaluation. Consequently, the athletes from countries with low birth rates collected on an average more points per participation than did those from countries with higher birth rates.

Figure 21 shows the relation between the point rate and birth rate for each country. Some countries with low birth rate, like Sweden, collected high numbers of athletic achievement points per million inhabitants. *The analysis of the data for the 1952 Olympic Games does not support claims to the effect that low birth rates necessarily reflect a low vitality of a nation.*

MEDICAL OBSERVATIONS

Through the courtesy of the Finnish Association of Sports Physicians we were given access to the medical data collected during the 1952 Games. No case of severe or permanent damage to the health of the competitors was encountered. Since there has been much concern about »strain» and »overstrain» through athletics, and recently also of »diseases of adaptation», the *innuendo* of the use of such terms being that strenuous physical exercise and training may give rise to distinct though hitherto unspecified pathological conditions, it is important to state that

POINT RATE

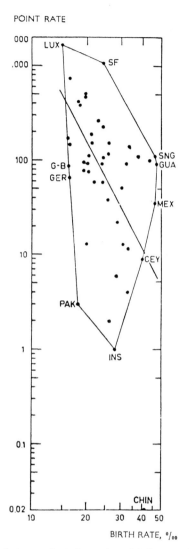

Fig. 21. Point rate (y) as plotted against birth-rate (x), *pro mille.* The straight line expresses the regression equation:

$$\log y \simeq \text{constant} - 1.84 \log x.$$

A definite negative correlation is observable.

POINT RATE

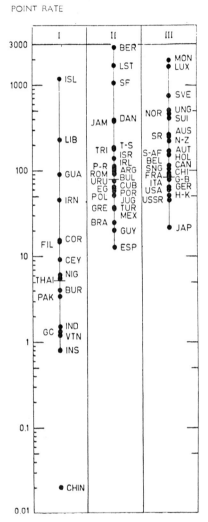

Fig. 22. Point rate of countries of different types of economy. The short horizontal lines represent the average point rate of each type of economy. I: Prevailing subsistence economy, II: Primarily agricultural economy, III: Agricultural-industrial and primarily industrial economy.

nothing of the sort was seen at Helsinki. If in fact such clinical syndromes exist in well trained sportsmen and -women, they should have been in evidence at the Olympic Games where the highest athletic performance standards of all times were attained.

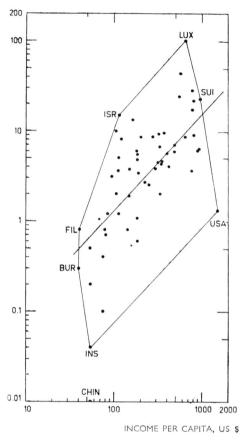

Fig. 23. Participation rate (*y*) as plotted against national income per capita (*x*), U.S. $. The straight line represents the regression equation:
$$\log y \simeq \text{constant} + 1.11 \log x.$$
A marked positive correlation is observable.

In most track and field and in most swimming competitions Olympic records and in many instances world records were broken. But nobody »overstrained« his heart, no attack of *angina pectoris* or of coronary occlusion occurred, nobody died from exertion, none of the woman athletes, none of the 13 and 14 year old boy and girl competitors and none of the participants of age 60 and above required medical attention. Without exception the

POINT RATE

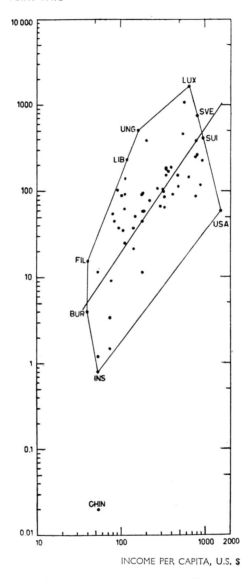

INCOME PER CAPITA, U.S. $

Fig. 24. Point rate (y) as plotted against national income per capita (x), U.S. $. The straight line expresses the regression equation:
$$\log y \simeq \text{constant} + 1.46 \log x.$$
A definite positive correlation is evident.

winners in the various events finished in conspicuously good physical condition. According to the official report of the Games, no case of collapse was encountered among Olympic competitors through three cases of collapse of officials and seven cases of collapse of spectators had to be treated by the attending physicians.[1] Altogether the talk-of »dangers of competitive athletics», whether for men or for women, for young or for old, represents much ado about nothing.

That the presence of pathological conditions of long standing or of infectious diseases may give rise to unusual responses to physical effort is unquestioned. However, not a single instance of this kind came to the attention of the physicians on duty during the Olympic Games, a fact which reflects the rarity of such happenings and the large margin of safety on which one can rely.

At least one severely disabled competitor attained top honors in an Olympic event, viz. the Danish riding champion Mrs. Lis Hartel who came second in dressage. Mrs. Hartel who retained extensive permanent atrophic and paralytic remnants of a poliomyelitic infection during early adulthood repeated her Olympic success in Helsinki in 1952 during the equestrian competitions in Stockholm in June 1956. She came again second in the Grand Prix de Dressage.

This case which has many parallels in the history of the Olympic Games reflects the magnitude of the compensatory powers which can be called upon in physically disabled individuals. The entire physiological and clinical theory underlying modern rehabilitation is based on the appreciation of the fact that it is the sum total of a person's abilities that counts and not, or at least not necessarily, his or her disabilities.

ECONOMIC CONDITIONS

Type of Economy

In order to obtain information on the interrelations between rates of participation and achievements in the 1952 Olympic Games and economic conditions, groups of countries with corres-

---

[1] Kolkka, p. 193.

ponding types of economy were studied and the results analyzed in terms of varying patterns of industrialization. Following Woytinsky & Woytinsky's procedure[1] a distinction was made between four main types of economy, viz.

1) *subsistence economy,* as prevails in the largest parts of Asia and Africa, on the Pacific Islands and in some regions of Latin America;

2) *primarily agricultural economy,* as is found predominantly in the Western Hemisphere: mainly south of the Rio Grande; in the Eastern Hemisphere; in Spain and Portugal, south-eastern Europe and the Mediterranean strip of Africa.

3) *primarily industrial economy,* as present in Switzerland, Western Germany, Belgium, Luxembourg and United Kingdom which countries form a continuous strip of Western Europe;

4) *agricultural-industrial economy* in a large number of countries dispersed all over the world, as shown in Appendix 5 and Figure 22.

Since differentiation between industrial and agricultural-industrial is irrelevant for our purposes, we have combined the groups 3 and 4.

Table 23 summarizes the findings. The countries on the top level of economic development showed the highest participation and point rates at the 1952 Olympic Games. *Countries with subsistence economy* contributed only six per cent of the total number of participations and collected *only four per cent of the point aggregate.* In interpreting these figures, it must be realized that the population of the underdeveloped countries *exceeds half of the total population* represented at the 1952 Olympic Games. *The point rate* (Fig. 22) is much higher for the economically developed countries than it is for the countries with subsistence economy. Similarly, point level figures are higher for the countries with developed economy. However, the overall contribution to the Olympic Games, *in terms of point level,* of countries with subsistence economy, as against developed countries, dif-

---

[1] Woytinsky & Woytinsky, p. 434.

TABLE 23
TYPE OF ECONOMY AND OLYMPIC PARTICIPATION AND ACHIEVEMENT

Type of Economy	Population in Millions*	Particip- ations	Particip- ation Rate	Point Share	Point Rate	Point Level
prevailing subsistence economy............	1 098	197	0.18	3 304	3.0	16.8
primarily agricultural economy............	270	964	3.57	18 431	68.3	19.1
agricultural-industrial primarily industrial economy............	745	2 175	2.92	64 542	86.7	29.7

fered less than was expected (Table 23, last column) a result again revealing the interesting All-or-Nothing law of athletic achievement which was encountered in different connections in other analyses of this study (p. 110). This law ought to be of special interest to the historian suggesting explanations or possible explanations of past and present developments.

Income Per Capita

It is difficult to obtain reliable comparable data on national income on a global scale. Information is satisfactory for the economically advanced countries but quite unsatisfactory for the underdeveloped regions. For vast areas in the world no national income statistics whatever are available. For purposes of the present study such information as is contained in Woytinsky & Woytinsky's book[2] was supplemented by statistical data collected by the United Nations.[3] Still, no data at all or only crude approximate figures could be obtained for several of the countries which were represented at the Games. Significantly, virtually no information was obtained for the countries which were not represented at the Helsinki Games.

The *per capita* national income is indicative of the economic status of a country, notwithstanding the fact that non-economic factors (*e.g.*, age distribution of the population) may to some extent affect the picture.

---

[2] Woytinsky & Woytinsky, p. 389-390.
[3] Yearbook of UN 1953, p. 56.

Medical Sociology of Sport

TABLE 24
PER CAPITA INCOME AND OLYMPIC PARTICIPATION AND ACHIEVEMENT

Per Capita Income in Dollars, 1948	Population in Millions	Particip- ations	Particip- ation Rate	Point Share	Point Rate	Poin. Level
Less than 60	617	55	0.09	969	1.6	17.6
60— 99	478	105	0.22	1 825	3.8	17.4
100—199	377	609	1.62	10 566	28.0	17.3
200—499	521	1 451	2.79	41 517	79.7	28.6
500—749	113	922	8.16	22 384	198.1	24.3
750 and over	152	194	1.28	9 016	59.4	46.5

Table 24 and Figures 23 and 24 summarize the data for *per capita* income and for participation and achievements at the 1952 Olympic Games. The majority of allocations for participation and of points collected in athletic contests had to be credited to countries with developed economy. Table 24 shows how small participation and point rates were for the large areas of the world in which *per capita* income is lowest. As to the average point value of a single participation, the picture is less clearly differentiated. Averages are higher for countries with high income, though there are noteworthy exceptions.

Geographical Distance from the Participating Countries to Helsinki

Although modern technical developments have »shortened» geographical distances and made travel easier, the vast distances between Finland and the countries on the opposite side of the earth may, it was thought, have affected rates of participation at the Helsinki Games.

Distances from Helsinki were »measured» in terms of the price of a return air ticket from the various countries' capitals to Finland.[4] In a few cases, prices of air tickets were not available. Then »calculated prices» were determined by means of statistical

---

[4] Aero Oy, 1952.

PARTICIPATION RATE

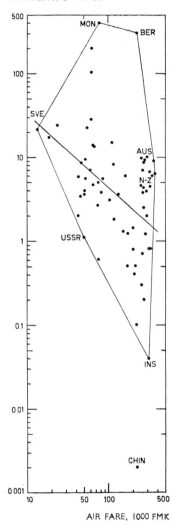

Fig. 25. Participation rate (y) as plotted against return air fare from the respective countries' capitals to Helsinki (x) thousands of Finnish Marks. The straight line represents the regression equation:

$$\log y \simeq \text{constant} - 0.89 \log x.$$

A tendency to a negative correlation is observable.

POINT RATE

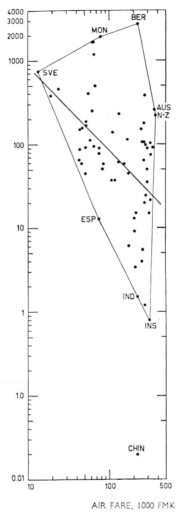

Fig. 26. Point rate (y) as plotted against return air fare from the respective countries' capitals to Helsinki (x), thousands of Finnish Marks. The straight line represents the regression equation:

$$\log y \simeq \text{constant} - 10.01 \log x.$$

A negative correlation is evident.

regression analysis which revealed the average dependence of air ticket prices on the shortest distance from the capital in question to Helsinki. Prices were expressed in thousands of Finnish Marks.

As Figures 25 and 26 illustrate, a negative correlation was observed between geographical distance, participation and point rate. The scatter of the dots around the regression lines is rather large. Also, the fact that most of the economically better situated countries lie nearer to Finland as compared with low level economies introduced an extraneous variation factor. The negative correlation under reference must therefore be considered, at least in part, due to factors other than that of geographical distance. The fact simply is that the majority of the leading sporting nations are situated in the geographical vicinity of Finland; and that the USA and the USSR sent full teams to the Games. From the point of view of international athletics it is still possible to sit in Europe and speak of »the periphery of the world», though the global picture is rapidly changing as has been detailed before.

CONCLUSION

The late General Smuts[1] presented a philosophical system based on the conviction that progressive historical and social developments follow the integration of small political or geographic entities into larger wholes. He referred to this concept as »Holism». The evolution of the British Empire or, as he preferred to call it in his later years, the British Commonwealth, of the United States of America, of the League of Nations which he had helped to bring into existence, and of the United Nations were looked upon by him as vivid examples for the validity of his theory.

The Olympic movement is based upon the acceptance of national representation from countries and societies all over the globe, and small and smallest units are encouraged to send teams of their own alongside the large powers. The latter, in turn, are

---

[1] Smuts, 1926.

expected to do likewise within the confines of their administrative and constitutional spheres of responsibility. Of all the colonial powers Great Britain was represented by the largest number of autonomous units at the Olympic Games, in addition to the fact that the Dominions of the British Commonwealth entered national teams of their own. By contrast, France failed to open corresponding channels of self-assertion, even to such highly developed societies as those of Algiers, Tunis and Morocco. Similarly, Portugal's ancient colonies of Angola and Mozambique in Africa and Goa in Asia were not enabled to send national teams to Helsinki. The International Olympic Committee itself follows a liberal and generous policy in readily allowing independent status to newly formed national entities as the acceptance in 1952 of representation from Libya, Israel, Gold Coast and the Netherlands' Antilles illustrated.

Huizinga[2] holds that the study of history reveals a pattern, adherence to or deviation from which decides whether a society will survive, or fail to survive, in its continuous struggle. This pattern carries the characteristics of play in that freedom and independence of collective action establish themselves only on the firm basis of rules or, in political parlance, of constitutional self-discipline. Without rules no freedom and without freedom no long-term survival. The modern sports movement offers such a pattern of freedom based upon rules, and by accepting this pattern societies can harness the vitality of their people and thus take a decisive step towards the progressive development of a cultural autonomy of their own.

Huizinga's concept provides a key for the understanding of such observations as the important part played in the Olympic movement by small countries; the flexible stability of the British in contrast to the French Empire; and of the reasons for the demand to form without delay National Olympic Committees in the territories under the jurisdiction of the Trusteeship Council of the United Nations.

The British historian Toynbee[3] has introduced the concept of

---

[2] Huizinga, 1939.
[3] Toynbee, 1947.

challenges which, as he points out, test the staying power of nations, challenges to which they respond in their own way, maintaining their status, progresssing or declining as the case may be. Our Olympic survey provides an illustration for the critical significance of Toynbee's theory, in that it reveals a generally retarding effect of a hot climate upon physical efficiency but at the same time demonstrates impressive examples of societies and individuals who overcome this handicap. Though statistically the preponderance of Olympic participants and winners from the cold countries is overwhelming, a number of Olympic finalists came from Uruguay and Brazil, from Jamaica and Mexico, from Venezuela and Cuba, from Trinidad and the Bahamas. Among them were black and white and yellow-brown athletes. The significance of this observation lies in the fact that it permits a new estimate of the developmental possibilities of the vast aggregate of 1,000 million inhabitants of the hot regions of the world. In future days the remarkable athletes whose performances are enumerated in Table 17 will be looked upon as pioneers who have proved to the world that climatic conditions which for millennia were regarded as insuperable obstacles to the attainment of supreme levels of physical fitness and thus of social advancement can be coped with.

Lewin,[4] a social psychologist of renown, held that cultured and intellectually differentiated individuals are distinguished from less advanced subjects in that they are capable of holding multiple loyalties which they integrate with the deep and abiding loyalty to the society to which they belong. The great figures from the history of the ethical religions of the world are impressive examples of the validity of Lewin's philosophical hypothesis which also seems to apply to collectives. The enthusiasm with which men and women all over the world respond to the Olympic call is indicative of a process of social, cultural and political maturation, in the very sense in which Lewin understood these terms. In the Olympic movement a universal ideological structure is being built up from large as well as from small component

---

[4] Lewin, 1948.

units. It is this kind of pattern which Smuts had in mind when he spoke of holism.

In formulating and guiding the policy of the Olympic Games the International Olympic Committee has made a moral contribution to mankind which is comparable to those made by the International Red Cross and by the Quakers who have enlarged the scope of individual dignity and of world peace, though of course by different means. The International Olympic Committee has thus earned the appreciation of the world which, it is hoped, will find appropriate formal expression.

APPENDIX 1
Basic Data

Country	Abbreviation of name of country	Population in millions, about 1952 [a]	Individual competition					Calories per head per day about 1950 [b]	Per capita income about 1948 US $ [c]	Death rate per 1000 inhabitants, about 1950	Infant mortality per 1000 live births, about 1940	Birth rate per 1000 inhabitants, about 1950 [d]	Return air fare from capital to Helsinki, thousands of Finnish marks, in 1952 [e]
			Participations	Point share	Participation rate	Point rate	Point level						
Argentina	ARG	17.2	78	1 814	4.5	106	23.3	3 110	315	9.1	90	24.9	327
Australia	AUS	8.2	74	2 172	9.0	265	29.4	3 165b_1	812	9.6	39	23.3	366
Austria	AUT	7.1	68	1 206	9.5	170	17.7	2 730	368	12.7	72	15.8	52e_1
Belgium	BEL	8.6	74	1 347	8.6	157	18.2	2 950	646	12.4	92	16.5	47
Bermuda	BER	0.04a_1	12	112	300.0	2 800	9.3	oo	oo	oo	oo	oo	226e_1
Brazil	BRA	52.1	61	1 286	1.2	25	21.1	2 343b_2	112	oo	182	oo	285
British Guiana	GUY	0.4	1	8	2.5	20	8.0	oo	oo	oo	oo	oo	274e_1
Bulgaria	BUL	7.2	36	659	0.5	92	18.3	oo	113	13.4	137	24.0	75e_1
Burma	BUR	18.5	5	74	0.3	4	14.8	oo	40	23.0	208	32.4	254
Canada	CAN	13.8	83	1 647	6.0	116	19.8	3 130	895	9.0	57	26.6	163
Ceylon	CEY	7.5	6	69	0.8	9	11.5	oo	79	12.6	150	40.3	203
Chile	CHI	5.8	35	535	6.0	92	15.3	oo	180	15.7	222	32.4	347
China	CHIN	463.5	1	11	—	0.02	11.0	2 030b_{11}	54c_1	..	..	40.7	224e_1
Cuba	CUB	5.3	20	342	3.8	65	17.1	..	296	..	127	..	270e_1
Czechoslovakia	T-S	12.6	71	2 386	5.6	189	33.6	..	345	11.7	..	22.1	52
Denmark	DAN	4.3	74	1 664	17.2	387	22.5	3 168b_{18}	781	9.2	50	18.6	19
Egypt	EG	20.4	73	1 258	3.6	62	17.2	2 475b_3	112	20.3	162	..	132
Finland	SF	4.1	179	4 436	43.5	1 082	24.8	3 213b_{16}	569	10.2	85	24.0	—
France	FRA	41.9	169	3 858	4.0	92	22.8	2 680b_{14}	418	12.6	92	20.4	51
Great Britain	G-B	50.6	180	4 392	3.6	87	24.4	3 060b_7	777	11.7	57	16.1	50
Gold Coast	G-C	3.7	5	49	1.4	13	9.8	..	..	21.3	..	30.7	204e_1
Germany	GER	69.0	139	4 486	2.0	65	32.3	2 840	336	10.4	64	16.2	43
Greece	GRE	8.0	25	301	3.1	38	12.0	2 500	95	10.7	122	26.1	107
Guatemala	GUA	2.8	28	255	10.0	91	9.1	..	103	21.5	110	48.7	299e_1
Hong Kong	H-K	2.3	9	117	3.9	51	13.0	..	..	..	..	..	295
Hungary	UNG	9.3	125	4 702	13.4	506	37.8	..	163	11.2	128	19.1	67
Iceland	ISL	0.1 a_2	14	120	140.0	1 200	8.6	3 240	..	7.9	34	..	64
India	IND	358.0	37	553	0.1	2	14.9	1 850b_6	75	16.0	160	26.7	224
Indonesia	INS	73.5	3	57	0.04	1	19.0	1 880b_5	54c_1	20.3	..	28.3	317e_1
Iran	IRN	18.8	22	849	1.2	45	38.6	..	85c_1	..	..	..	174
Ireland	IRL	3.0	21	338	7.0	113	16.1	3 560	485	12.6	68	21.0	59
Israel	ISR	1.3	19	182	15.0	140	9.6	2 500b_8	114c_1	6.5	..	32.9	110e_1
Italy	ITA	46.3	123	3 610	2.7	78	29.3	2 343b_9	225	9.8	103	19.6	74
Jamaica	JAM	1.4	12	542	8.6	387	45.2	..	201	11.8	..	..	274e_1
Japan	JAP	82.9	64	1 791	0.8	22	28.0	2 100b_{10}	143	11.0	88	28.4	328
Korea	COR	29.5	15	447	0.5	15	29.8	..	54c_1	21.2	..	31.8	215e_1
Lebanon	LIB	1.1	9	255	8.2	232	28.3	..	118	..	..	..	132
Liechtenstein	LST	0.01a_3	2	17	200.0	1 700	8.5	..	..	..	..	..	63e_1
Luxembourg	LUX	0.3	31	506	102.0	1 687	16.3	2 950	646	11.6	..	14.8	62e_1
Mexico	MEX	25.4	50	894	2.0	35	17.9	..	106	16.4	127	45.7	297e_1

APPENDIX 1
BASIC DATA

Country	Abbreviation of name of country	Population in millions, about 1952a	Individual competition					Calories per head per day about 1950 b	Per capita income about 1948 US$ c	Death rate per 1000 inhabitants, about 1950	Infant mortality per 1000 live births, about 1940	Birth rate per 1000 inhabitants, about 1950 d	Return air fare from capital to Helsinki, thousands of Finnish marks, in 1952 e
			Participations	Point share	Participation rate	Point rate	Point level						
Monaco	MON	0.02	8	39	400.0	1 950	4.9	..	..	..	..	..	78e1
Netherlands	HOL	10.1	59	1 573	5.9	152	28.1	2 901b4	487	7.5	39	22.7	43
New Zealand	N-Z	1.9	12	429	6.3	226	35.8	3 260b19	933	9.3	28	24.6	374
Nigeria	NIG	24.0	11	146	0.5	6	13.3	..	..	..	..	..	174
Norway	NOR	3.3	79	1 522	24.0	461	19.3	3 120	550	8.9	39	19.3	24
Pakistan	PAK	75.0	28	254	0.4	3	9.0	2 020b12	69	12.3	..	18.0	211
Philippines	FIL	19.6	15	296	0.8	15	19.7	..	41	..	..	..	353
Poland	POL	25.0	84	1 477	3.4	59	17.5	..	190	..	143	..	16
Portugal	POR	8.5	47	499	5.5	59	10.6	2 110b13	184c1	..	126	24.2	45
Puerto Rico	P-R	2.2	21	236	9.6	107	11.2	..	275	9.9	..	38.5	285e1
Rumania	ROM	16.1	76	1 530	4.7	95	20.1	..	184c1	20.0	190	19.6	65e1
Saar	SR	1.0 a3	28	255	28.0	255	9.1	..	770c2	..	..	..	62e1
Singapore	SNG	1.0	7	105	7.0	105	15.0	..	..	12.1	..	45.7	267
South Africa	S-AF	12.3	56	1 878	4.6	153	33.5	2 700	347	8.6	50	25.7	251
Spain	ESP	28.3	17	359	0.6	13	21.1	2 760	182	10.8	110	19.9	75
Sweden	SVE	7.0	151	5 253	21.5	750	34.8	3 070b15	805	10.1	39	16.4	13
Switzerland	SUI	4.7	105	1 962	22.5	417	18.7	3 096b17	950	10.1	46	18.1	56
Thailand	THAI	18.3	12	100	0.7	6	8.3	..	81	10.6	..	27.1	261
Trinidad	TRI	0.7 a1	3	127	4.3	181	42.3	..	..	..	..	..	269e1
Turkey	TUR	20.9	31	779	1.9	37	24.4	2 650	143	..	..	..	117
United States	USA	151.7	194	9 016	1.3	59	46.5	3 120	1 525	9.6	47	23.4	154
Uruguay	URU	2.4	16	182	6.7	76	11.4	..	331	8.3	85	20.7	327
USSR	USSR	193.0	209	8 690	1.1	45	41.6	..	181	..	..	..	50
Venezuela	VNZ	4.9	45	485	9.2	99	10.8	..	322	11.0	124	43.1	280e1
Viet-Nam	VTN	30.5 a4	7	38	0.2	1	5.4	..	54c1	21.6	..	..	273
Yugoslavia	JUG	16.3	53	832	3.8	51	15.7	..	150c1	13.1	130	30.2	82

Appendix 1 footnotes

a Woytinsky & Woytinsky, 1953, pp. 48-49

a_1 Statistical Yearbook of Finland, 1954, p. 327

a_2 Statistical Yearbook of Finland, 1954, p. 331

a_3 Statistical Yearbook of Finland, 1954, p. 328

a_4 Statistical Yearbook of Finland, 1954, p. 329

b Statistical Yearbook of Finland, 1955, p. 404

b_1 Russell, 1954, p. 420

b_2 Russell, 1954, p. 461
b_3 Russell, 1954, p. 180
b_4 Russell, 1954, p. 95
b_5 Russell, 1954, p. 351
b_6 Russell, 1954, p. 129
b_7 Russell, 1954, p. 25
b_8 Russell, 1954, p. 168
b_9 Russell, 1954, p. 155
b_{10} Russell, 1954, p. 350
b_{11} Russell, 1954, p. 347
b_{12} Russell, 1954, p. 341
b_{13} Russell, 1954, p. 150
b_{14} Russell, 1954, p. 138
b_{15} Russell, 1954, p. 119

b_{16} Russell, 1954, p. 130
b_{17} Russell, 1954, p. 155
b_{18} Russell, 1954, p. 107
b_{19} Russell, 1954, p. 442

c Woytinsky & Woytinsky, p. 392-39
c_1 Woytinsky & Woytinsky, p. 434
c_2 Official information from th Government of the Saar

d Woytinsky & Woytinsky

e Aero Oy 1952
e_1 See page 101

APPENDIX 2

INDIVIDUAL COMPETITIONS. POINT SHARE BY COUNTRY AND SPORT. THE COUNTRIES ARE LISTED IN THE ORDER OF TOTAL INDIVIDUAL POINT SHARE

Country	Shooting	Canoeing, men	Canoeing, ladies	Fencing, men	Fencing, ladies	Modern pentathlon	Boxing	Free style wrestling	Greco-Roman wrestling	Weight-lifting	Cycling	Equestrian	Rowing	Swimming, men	Swimming, ladies	Gymnastics, men	Gymnastics, ladies	Track and field, men	Track and field, ladies	Total, men	Total, ladies	Total
1. United States	408	157	30	212	148	133	645	423	·	584	29	224	241	372	809	159	63	3 355	241	7 725	1 291	9 016
2. USSR	726	71	57	144	65	99	513	464	637	597	35	75	100	478	225	518	546	2 018	1 322	6 475	2 215	8 690
3. Sweden	618	245	6	258	140	182	240	448	448	127	77	410	·	212	155	58	195	1 472	102	4 795	458	5 253
4. Hungary	398	150	·	478	31	190	262	160	441	41	61	·	·	179	687	225	395	801	118	3 386	1 340	4 726
5. Germany	190	144	19	70	·	20	355	244	204	86	186	·	·	262	141	262	162	1 001	734	3 399	1 087	4 486
6. Finland	642	251	100	118	15	143	464	189	377	93	29	17	6	142	82	295	66	1 238	169	4 004	432	4 436
7. Great Britain	191	32	6	177	65	52	217	109	3	77	145	217	52	414	432	48	36	1 639	480	3 373	1 019	4 392
8. France	180	107	6	402	113	36	199	55	83	126	153	341	6	511	217	107	86	932	198	3 238	620	3 858
9. Italy	202	14	·	586	136	29	531	82	288	117	373	120	6	104	18	126	196	528	154	3 106	504	3 610
10. Czechoslovakia	172	229	24	·	·	·	211	50	148	76	26	·	24	76	·	233	268	718	131	1 963	423	2 386
11. Australia	424	·	·	96	10	18	82	57	·	116	197	·	76	377	131	·	·	471	541	1 490	682	2 172
12. Switzerland	14	12	6	158	5	58	51	69	·	10	74	209	24	53	40	369	·	367	33	1 878	84	1 962
13. South Africa	195	·	46	·	·	—	398	158	·	97	116	·	44	300	192	7	·	250	302	1 384	494	1 878
14. Argentina	31	·	·	135	17	58	231	131	12	195	88	188	·	103	54	9	·	270	128	1 615	199	1 814
15. Japan	·	31	·	19	·	·	17	303	12	·	5	3	·	660	106	222	·	332	93	1 592	199	1 791
16. Denmark	110	61	37	147	80	·	110	45	50	65	153	149	·	61	269	93	·	189	45	1 233	431	1 664
17. Canada	265	62	·	33	·	·	167	57	·	161	36	47	24	187	75	·	·	371	186	1 386	261	1 647
18. Netherlands	·	81	·	·	·	·	138	·	174	18	130	21	·	134	482	52	58	139	302	685	888	1 573
19. Rumania	307	10	·	177	·	·	313	6	66	18	69	21	·	9	·	96	107	197	76	1 347	183	1 530
20. Norway	492	53	·	68	·	·	88	·	·	30	52	32	·	51	·	·	9	461	18	1 495	27	1 522
21. Poland	59	·	·	189	27	·	331	·	63	10	·	·	62	65	22	82	132	274	161	1 135	342	1 477
22. Belgium	78	50	·	237	·	3	83	75	88	3	306	·	24	10	81	9	·	300	·	1 266	81	1 347
23. Brazil	143	·	·	35	·	77	143	133	·	25	·	107	·	295	43	·	·	328	90	1 153	133	1 286
24. Egypt	106	·	·	205	·	·	80	·	152	272	·	60	6	108	·	56	·	80	·	1 258	·	1 258
25. Austria	118	32	73	148	93	·	88	·	70	58	12	·	·	68	17	114	79	96	140	804	402	1 206

APPENDIX 2

INDIVIDUAL COMPETITIONS. POINT SHARE BY COUNTRY AND SPORT. THE COUNTRIES ARE LISTED IN THE ORDER OF TOTAL INDIVIDUAL POINT SHARE

Country	Shooting	Canoeing, men	Canoeing, ladies	Fencing, men	Fencing, ladies	Modern pentathlon	Boxing	Free style wrestling	Greco-Roman wrestling	Weight-lifting	Cycling	Equestrian	Rowing	Swimming, men	Swimming, ladies	Gymnastics, men	Gymnastics, ladies	Track and field, men	Track and field, ladies	Total, men	Total, ladies	Total
26. Mexico	120	·	·	92	·	14	56	55	·	20	4	105	·	383	24	·	·	19	2	868	26	894
27. Iran	·	·	·	·	·	·	91	386	·	351	·	·	·	·	·	·	·	21	·	849	·	849
28. Yugoslavia	129	19	·	·	·	·	94	·	44	·	·	·	·	94	·	41	74	290	47	711	121	832
29. Turkey	·	·	·	·	·	·	·	418	167	·	·	·	·	·	·	·	·	170	·	755	·	755
30. Bulgaria	105	·	·	·	·	·	122	·	·	·	3	32	·	·	·	116	188	54	39	432	227	659
31. India	43	·	·	·	·	·	85	137	·	22	4	·	·	51	27	—	·	148	36	490	63	553
32. Jamaica	·	·	·	·	·	·	·	·	·	·	13	·	·	·	·	·	·	506	23	519	23	542
33. Chile	42	·	·	·	·	65	·	·	·	·	18	243	6	9	·	·	·	113	39	496	39	535
34. Luxembourg	·	10	·	125	·	·	40	·	17	·	71	·	·	10	·	65	·	168	·	506	·	506
35. Portugal	59	·	·	92	·	9	·	·	·	·	·	164	·	59	·	8	6	102	·	493	6	499
36. Venezuela	78	·	·	57	10	·	90	21	·	·	20	·	·	9	·	·	·	200	·	475	10	485
37. Korea	·	·	·	·	·	·	144	6	·	193	·	4	·	·	·	·	·	95	5	442	5	447
38. New Zealand	·	·	·	·	·	·	·	·	·	24	31	·	·	35	65	·	·	111	163	201	228	429
39. Spain	134	·	·	·	·	·	·	·	·	·	·	124	·	62	·	23	·	10	·	359	·	359
40. Cuba	75	·	·	14	·	·	·	·	·	1	·	=	·	43	·	14	·	195	·	342	·	342
41. Ireland	·	·	·	48	·	·	182	6	·	·	·	54	·	·	·	·	·	48	·	338	·	338
42. Greece	80	·	·	·	·	·	·	·	36	·	·	·	·	·	·	·	·	185	·	301	·	301
43. Philippines	118	·	·	·	·	·	69	4	·	92	·	·	·	13	·	·	·	·	·	296	·	296
44. Guatemala	84	·	·	38	·	·	·	20	22	·	7	·	·	9	·	·	·	57	18	237	18	255
45. Lebanon	20	·	·	·	·	·	7	·	181	47	·	·	·	·	·	·	·	·	·	255	·	255
46. Saar	18	·	14	42	·	·	40	·	51	·	·	·	24	9	·	26	·	16	15	226	29	255
47. Pakistan	—	·	·	·	·	·	80	·	·	7	6	·	·	32	·	·	·	127	·	252	·	252
48. Puerto Rico	60	·	·	·	·	·	55	·	·	34	·	·	·	·	·	·	·	87	·	236	·	236
49. Israel	31	·	·	·	·	·	·	·	·	·	·	·	·	49	·	·	·	85	17	165	17	182
50. Uruguay	·	·	·	27	·	23	26	·	·	·	36	·	24	22	·	·	·	2	22	160	22	182

No. & Country																						
51. Nigeria	146	.	146	.	146	.	.	.	.	.	.	.	.	.	.	.	.	.	.	.	.	.
52. Trinidad	127	.	127	.	.	.	.	.	.	.	.	.	127	.	.	.	.	.	.	.	.	.
53. Iceland	120	.	120	.	120	.	.	.	.	.	.	.	.	.	.	.	.	.	.	.	.	.
54. Hong Kong	117	31	86	.	.	.	.	31	86	.	.	.	.	.	.	.	.	.	.	.	.	.
55. Bermuda	112	33	79	33	.	.	.	.	79	.	.	.	.	.	.	.	.	.	.	.	.	.
56. Singapore	105	18	87	18	.	.	.	.	18	.	.	.	69	.	.	.	.	.	.	.	.	.
57. Thailand	100	.	100	.	100	.	.	.	.	.	.	.	.	.	.	.	.	.	.	.	.	.
58. Burma	74	.	74	.	.	.	.	.	.	.	.	.	32	.	42	.	.	.	.	.	.	.
59. Ceylon	69	.	69	.	.	.	.	.	35	.	.	.	.	.	34	.	.	.	.	.	.	.
60. Indonesia	57	.	57	.	13	.	.	.	10	.	.	.	34	.	.	.	.	.	.	.	.	.
61. Gold Coast	49	.	49	.	49	.	.	.	.	.	.	.	.	.	.	.	.	.	.	.	.	39
62. Monaco	39	.	39	.	.	.	.	.	18	.	.	.	.	.	13	.	.	.	5	.	.	.
63. Viet-Nam	38	.	38	.	.	.	.	.	.	.	.	2	.	.	.	.	.	.	.	.	.	.
64. Liechtenstein	17	.	17	.	.	.	.	.	.	.	.	17	.	.	.	.	.	.	.	.	.	.
65. China	11	.	11	.	.	.	.	.	11	.	.	.	.	.	.	.	.	.	.	.	.	.
66. British Guiana	8	.	8	.	.	.	.	.	.	.	.	.	3	.	.	.	.	.	.	.	.	.
67. Panama	—	.	—	.	.	.	.	.	.	.	.	.	.	.	.	.	.	.	.	.	.	.
Total	87 407	14 711	72 696	6 241	21 064	2 666	3 433	4 425	7 377	538	3 342	2 584	4 063	3 822	4 311	7 227	1 209	955	4 632	424	1 790	7 304

APPENDIX 3

TEAM COMPETITIONS. POINT SHARE BY COUNTRY AND BY SPORT. THE COUNTRIES ARE LISTED IN THE ORDER OF TOTAL TEAM POINT SHARE

	Games playing				Canoeing	Fencing	Modern pentathlon	Yachting	Cycling	Equestrian	Rowing	Swimming		Gymnastics		Track and field			Total, men	Total, ladies	Total
	Football	Basketball	Field hockey	Water-polo								4×200 m relay, men	4×100 m relay, ladies	Men	Ladies	4×100 m relay, men	4×400 m relay, men	4×100 m relay, ladies			
1. United States	5	100	·	54	65	95	49	292	12	113	333	100	57	34	2	100	76	100	1 428	159	1 587
2. France	5	34	25	·	192	182	8	76	158	63	294	61	19	21	10	47	38	15	1 204	44	1 248
3. Sweden	66	·	·	18	161	99	74	280	58	213	60	51	30	10	50	64	14	15	1 104	95	1 199
4. Hungary	100	21	25	100	140	204	100	·	42	·	50	43	100	43	75	9	14	·	921	175	1 096
5. Germany	57	·	25	·	195	45	·	126	37	150	146	·	24	56	42	9	62	74	908	140	1 048
6. Italy	23	4	4	64	12	250	11	194	230	—	137	9	6	27	35	9	14	15	988	56	1 044
7. Great Britain	5	56	54	18	16	81	15	147	100	100	206	37	37	3	—	54	44	59	880	96	976
8. USSR	23	78	·	36	71	17	41	36	12	11	230	9	·	100	100	77	14	49	755	149	904
9. Finland	23	21	4	·	204	19	59	101	18	—	166	9	6	65	7	9	14	15	712	28	740
10. Denmark	44	·	·	·	153	67	·	156	102	10	144	·	46	14	·	·	·	·	690	46	736
11. Switzerland	·	4	4	·	14	69	19	86	62	67	149	·	·	78	·	9	14	·	575	·	575
12. Argentina	·	56	·	18	·	63	23	138	12	35	152	27	·	·	·	28	·	15	552	15	567
13. Belgium	23	4	25	41	10	99	·	13	148	·	147	9	6	·	·	·	14	·	510	6	516
14. Netherlands	5	·	71	47	53	·	·	134	61	·	32	·	73	16	5	·	·	34	403	112	515
15. Norway	23	·	·	·	89	19	·	292	10	·	49	·	·	·	·	·	·	·	498	·	498
16. Czechoslovakia	·	21	·	·	132	·	·	·	·	·	142	·	·	38	60	41	·	·	374	60	434
17. Austria	44	·	25	18	140	39	·	65	18	·	22	·	·	24	17	·	·	·	395	17	412
18. Canada	·	21	·	·	108	·	·	100	·	·	32	9	6	·	·	9	52	15	331	21	352
19. Australia	·	·	·	3	·	17	·	24	112	·	108	9	·	6	13	9	14	41	296	41	337
20. Yugoslavia	78	·	·	77	·	·	·	8	·	·	121	·	·	·	·	·	·	·	290	13	303
21. Brazil	44	43	·	18	·	6	34	83	·	50	7	9	·	·	·	·	·	·	294	·	294
22. South Africa	·	·	·	18	·	·	·	47	151	·	4	31	·	·	·	28	14	·	265	·	265
23. Poland	23	·	4	·	·	45	·	·	·	·	75	9	·	19	25	28	·	15	203	40	243

	1	2	3	4	5	6	7	8	9	10	11	12	13	14	15	16	17	18	19	20	21
24. Portugal	23	·	·	3	·	12	—	156	·	48	6	·	·	—	·	9	·	·	234	·	234
25. Egypt	·	21	·	18	·	77	·	·	·	10	14	·	·	12	·	9	·	·	184	·	184
26. Chile	5	49	·	·	·	·	28	·	·	99	·	·	6	49	·	·	·	·	181	·	181
27. Japan	·	65	·	·	·	·	·	1	18	·	·	75	·	·	·	·	14	·	164	6	160
28. Uruguay	23	·	·	·	10	53	5	10	12	·	7	·	·	8	·	·	·	·	152	·	152
29. Luxembourg	·	·	·	·	·	·	·	·	24	·	60	·	·	·	·	·	14	·	132	·	132
30. India	5	·	100	3	·	·	·	·	12	·	·	·	·	·	·	·	·	·	120	·	120
31. Bulgaria	5	38	·	·	·	·	·	·	12	·	·	·	·	30	30	·	·	·	85	30	115
32. Cuba	·	21	·	·	·	·	·	59	·	17	·	·	·	·	·	28	·	·	108	·	108
33. Spain	·	·	·	32	·	·	·	31	·	·	7	·	·	1	·	·	·	·	87	·	87
34. Pakistan	·	·	42	·	·	·	·	·	·	·	·	·	·	·	·	28	14	·	84	·	84
35. Saar	·	·	·	·	24	11	·	·	·	·	29	·	·	·	·	·	·	15	65	15	80
36. Bahama	5	4	·	3	·	11	·	70	·	7	6	·	·	4	21	·	·	·	70	·	70
37. Rumania	·	·	·	3	·	·	3	·	3	21	·	·	·	7	·	·	·	·	43	21	64
38. Mexico	·	21	·	3	·	·	·	·	·	·	·	·	9	21	·	·	·	·	48	9	57
39. Turkey	44	4	·	·	·	·	·	·	·	·	·	·	·	·	·	·	·	·	48	·	48
40. Greece	5	4	·	18	·	·	·	13	·	·	7	·	·	·	·	·	·	·	47	·	47
41. New Zealand	·	·	·	·	·	·	·	·	30	·	7	·	·	·	·	·	·	·	37	·	37
42. Venezuela	·	·	·	·	·	17	·	·	12	·	·	·	·	·	·	28	·	·	29	·	29
43. Nigeria	·	·	·	·	·	·	·	·	·	·	·	·	·	·	·	·	·	·	28	·	28
44. Netherl. Antilles	23	·	·	·	·	·	·	·	·	·	·	·	·	·	·	·	·	·	23	·	23
45. Philippines	·	21	·	·	·	·	·	·	·	·	·	·	·	·	·	·	·	·	21	·	21
46. Guatemala	·	·	·	·	·	·	·	·	12	·	·	·	·	·	·	·	·	·	12	·	12
47. Gold Coast	·	·	·	·	·	·	·	·	·	·	·	·	·	·	·	9	·	·	9	·	9
48. Ireland	·	·	·	·	·	·	·	9	·	·	·	·	·	·	·	·	·	·	9	·	9
49. Thailand	·	·	·	·	·	·	·	·	·	·	·	·	·	·	·	9	·	·	9	·	9
50. Israel	·	4	·	·	·	·	·	·	·	·	·	·	·	·	·	·	·	·	4	·	4
51. Monaco	·	·	·	·	·	·	·	·	·	·	·	·	·	·	·	·	·	·	—	·	—
Total	706	659	383	610	1 789	1 597	469	2 747	1 478	1 014	2 949	497	425	658	492	613	440	477	16 609	1 394	18 003

Medical Sociology of Sport

APPENDIX 4
TEAM COMPETITIONS. POINT LEVELS OF COUNTRIES. THE COUNTRIES ARE
LISTED IN THE ORDER OF THEIR TEAM POINT LEVEL

Country	Point level	Country	Point level
1. Hungary	49.8	27. Turkey	24.0
2. United States	49.6	28. Banama	23.3
3. Czechoslovakia	43.5	29. Bulgaria	23.0
4. Norway	41.5	30. Netherlands	
5. Sweden	41.3	Antilles	23.0
6. France	39.0	31. Spain	21.8
7. Germany	38.8	32. Japan	21.3
8. Yougoslavia	37.9	33. Australia	21.1
9. Denmark	35.0	34. Philippines	21.0
10. Chile	34.2	35. Canada	20.7
11. South Africa	33.1	36. Poland	20.3
12. Italy	32.6	37. Luxembourg	18.9
13. Great Britain	32.5	38. New Zeland	18.5
14. Holland	32.2	39. Egypt	16.7
15. Argentina	31.5	40 Portugal	16.7
16. India	29.8	41. Guatenala	12.0
17. Austria	29.5	42. Mexico	11.4
18. USSR	29.2	43. Gold Coast	9.0
19. Nigeria	28.0	44. Ireland	9.0
20. Pakistan	28.0	45. Thailand	9.0
21. Belgium	27.2	46. Saar	8.0
22. Cuba	27.0	47. Greece	7.8
23. Brazil	26.7	48. Venezula	7.3
24. Switzerland	26.1	49. Rumania	6.0
25. Uruguay	25.3	50. Israel	4.0
26. Finland	24.7	51. Monaco	0.0

APPENDIX 5

DISTRIBUTION OF COUNTRIES AND REGIONS ACCORDING TO THE TYPE OF ECONOMY. REPRODUCED FROM WOYTINSKY & WOYTINSKY 1953, P. 434.

PREVAILING SUBSISTENCE ECONOMY

PER CAPITA INCOME, IN U.S. DOLLARS	COUNTRIES AND REGIONS	POPULATION IN MILLIONS	NATIONAL INCOME, IN MILLIONS OF U.S. DOLLARS
LESS THAN 60	PACIFIC ISLANDS, MOST OF AFRICA, SOME COLONIAL AREAS IN ASIA	160.0	7,640
	CHINA, MONGOLIA, KOREA, BHUTAN, NEPAL, BAHREIN, BURMA, INDOCHINA, INDONESIA, PHILIPPINES	641.5	34,800
	SAUDI ARABIA, YEMEN, AFGHANISTAN	25.0	1,370
	HAITI, ECUADOR AND FOREIGN POSSESSIONS IN AMERICA	9.6	500
OVER 60 TO 80	INDIA, PAKISTAN, CEYLON, THAILAND	445.5	33,021
	BOLIVIA	4.0	221
OVER 80 TO 100	IRAN, IRAQ	22.0	1,870
	PARAGUAY, PERU	8.4	770
OVER 100	GUATEMALA, SYRIA, LEBANON, JORDAN, TURKEY (IN ASIA)	23.3	2,750

PREVAILING MONEY ECONOMY

AGRICULTURAL-INDUSTRIAL ECONOMY

PER CAPITA INCOME, IN U.S. DOLLARS	COUNTRIES AND REGIONS	POPULATION IN MILLIONS	NATIONAL INCOME, IN MILLIONS OF U.S. DOLLARS
LESS THAN 300	JAPAN	80.2	11,523
	U.S.S.R.	193.0	35,000
	CHILE	5.6	1,013
	HUNGARY, ITALY	54.9	12,390
OVER 300 TO 500	AUSTRIA, CZECHOSLOVAKIA	19.3	6,800
	UNION OF SOUTH AFRICA	11.8	4,096
	FRANCE	41.5	17,336
OVER 500 TO 750	NETHERLANDS, NORWAY	13.0	6,516
OVER 750 TO 1000	DENMARK, SWEDEN	11.1	8,880
	CANADA (INCL. NEWFOUNDLAND), NEW ZEALAND, AUSTRALIA	22.5	19,550
OVER 1000	UNITED STATES	146.6	223,500

PRIMARILY INDUSTRIAL ECONOMY

PER CAPITA INCOME, IN U.S. DOLLARS	COUNTRIES AND REGIONS	POPULATION IN MILLIONS	NATIONAL INCOME, IN MILLIONS OF U.S. DOLLARS
LESS THAN 300			
OVER 300 TO 500	GERMANY	67.7	22,800
OVER 500 TO 750	BELGIUM AND LUXEMBOURG	8.8	5,690
OVER 750 TO 1000	UNITED KINGDOM, SWITZERLAND	54.6	43,365
OVER 1000			

PRIMARILY AGRICULTURAL ECONOMY

PER CAPITA INCOME, IN U.S. DOLLARS	COUNTRIES AND REGIONS	POPULATION IN MILLIONS	NATIONAL INCOME, IN MILLIONS OF U.S. DOLLARS
LESS THAN 150	EGYPT, ALGERIA, TUNISIA, MOROCCO, ISRAEL	41.2	4,700
	MEXICO, EL SALVADOR, HONDURAS, NICARAGUA, COSTA RICA, DOMINICAN REPUBLIC	31.0	3,310
	COLOMBIA, BRAZIL	60.0	6,986
	EUROPEAN TURKEY, GREECE, ALBANIA	10.6	1,300
OVER 150 TO 200	YUGOSLAVIA, BULGARIA	22.9	3,430
	PANAMA	0.7	125
	SPAIN, PORTUGAL, ROMANIA, POLAND	76.1	14,000
OVER 200 TO 300	CUBA, JAMAICA, PUERTO RICO	8.8	2,412
OVER 300	ARGENTINA, URUGUAY, VENEZUELA	23.1	7,325
	IRELAND, FINLAND	7.0	3,731

REFERENCES

Aero Oy: Tiedoitus No. 13. Asioimistoille ja matkatoimistoille, 1952.

Barnard, G. A.: The Theory of Information. *Journal of the Royal Statistical Society,* B: *13:*46, 1951.

de Beauvoir, S.: *The Second Sex.* New York, Alfred A. Knopf. 1953.

Berry, W. T. C., Beveridge, J. B., Bransby, E. R., Chalmers, A. K., Needman, B. M., Magee, H. E., Townsend, H. S. and Daubney, C. G.: The Diet, Haemoglobin Values and Blood Pressures of Olympic Athletes. *British Medical Journal, i:*300, 1949.

Casey, R. S. and Perry, J. W.: *Punched Cards. Their Applications to Science and Industry.* New York, Reinhold, 1951.

Chronicle of the WHO. A quantitative study of medical schools and physicians. *9:* 212, 1955.

Diem, C.: *Die Altersbreite der Körperleistungen. Leibesübungen, Sportarzt, Erziehung,* N:o 4-6 (April-June): 40, 1952.

Heine, Henrich: *Vermischte Schriften,* Vol. 13, I. Hamburg, Hoffman und Campe, 1876.

Huizinga, J.: *Homo Ludens.* Amsterdam, Pantheon Akademische Verlagsanstalt, 1939.

Huntington, E.: *Civilization and Climate.* 3rd edition. New Haven. Yale University Press, 1939.

Ingman, Ove: Menstruation in Finnish Top Class Sportswomen. *Sport Medicine,* Helsinki, 1953.

Jokl, E.: *Alter und Leistung.* Heidelberg, Springer, 1954.

Jokl, E.: The High Jump Technique of Central African Watussi. *Journal of Physical Education* (Glasgow), *33:*100, 1941.

Jokl, E.: Report of Activities of the Medical Research Committee of the National Advisory Council for Physical Education. *Manpower, 4:*2, 1946.

Karvonen, M. J.: Age and Performance in Athletics. *Internationale Zeitschrift für angewandte Physiologie, einschliesslich Arbeitsphysiologie, 16:*110, 1955.

Kolkka, S. (Editor): *The Official Report of the Organising Committee for the Games of the XV Olympiad Helsinki, 1952,* Porvoo, Helsinki, Werner Söderström, 1955.

Kral, I., and Markalous, E.: *Proc. II International Sports Medical Congress.* Leipzig, Berlin, 1936. Thieme, 1937.

Lewin, K.: *Resolving Social Conflicts.* New York, Harper, 1948.

Myrdal, G.: *An American Dilemma: The Negro Problem and Modern Democracy.* 2nd edition. New York, Harper, 1944.

Niemineva, K.: On the Course of Delivery of Finnish Baseball (pesä-pallo) Players and Swimmers. *Sport Medicine,* Helsinki, 1953.

XV Olympia Helsinki—Helsingfors 19. 7.—3. 8. *1952.* Bulletin No: 16, 1952.

Olympic Rules, Lausanne, International Olympic Committee, 1949.

Pfeifer, W. A.: Sportlicher Wettkampf und Geburtsverlauf. *Sport und Leiberserziehung,* 9/10 1951.

Russel, J.: *World Population and World Food Supplies.* London, George Allen and Unwin, 1954. *Scoring Table for Men's Track and Field Events.* Adopted by the Congress of the International Amateur Athletic Federation held in Brussels 1950 and Helsinki 1952. Stockholm, 1952.

Smuts, J. C.: *Holism, and Evolution.* London, McMillan, 1926.

Statistical Yearbook of Finland, New Series—50th—Year 1954. Helsinki, The Central Statistical Office, 1954.

Statistical Yearbook of Finland, New Series—51st—Year 1955. Helsinki, The Central Statistical Office, 1955.

Statistics of National Income and Expenditure. New York, Statistical Office of the United Nations, 1955.

Toynbee, A. J.: *A Study of History,* Vol. I—X. Oxford, Oxford University Press, 1934-1955.

Woytinsky, W. S., and Woytinsky, E. S.: *World Population and Production. Trends and Outlook,* New York, Twentieth Century Fund, 1953.

Yearbook of the United Nations 1953. New York, United Nations, 1953.

SPORT AND HUMAN DEVELOPMENT

ENDOSOMATIC AND EXOSOMATIC HEREDITY

The British biologist P. B. Medawar distinguishes between two systems of heredity. One he calls endosomatic (internal heredity), the other exosomatic (external heredity). The former, which we have in common with animals, is based upon the biologically predetermined interplay of chromosomes; the latter relates particularly to man and is passed from generation to generation through culture and tradition. No real change has taken place in the internal heredity of the human species during historical times. However, during the past two hundred years, the physical status of about one-third of mankind has become altered through several "external" factors, among them the vast improvements in diet and the conquests of infectious diseases that have occurred in our lifetime. As a direct result of these improvements, and their effect on the growth, fitness, health and longevity of large populations, a new basis has been created for remarkable advances in all measurable human performances.

FERNEL'S ALLEGORY

In 1548, the French philosopher Jean Fernel wrote as follows: "What geography is to history, such is anatomy to medicine. Both define theatres of events."

This statement suggests a twofold approach to a number of academic disciplines which deal with the structure, behaviour, content and meaning of certain phenomena. In so far as Fernel's allegory applies to the study of human movement, it must be realized that all movements contain a qualitative element which cannot easily be measured, and that any effective analysis of them must take us beyond the boundaries of the exact natural sciences. Man's seemingly unlimited capacity to express himself in, and attain his objectives through, movements, originates from concepts and images which require special techniques to be understood. The science of sport and physical education is thus confronted with an elementary dichotomy which it shares with only one other branch of science, namely neurophysiology. Both sport and physical education on the one hand and neurophysiology on the other ask *how mind obtains leverage upon matter.* This sort of leverage is possible only when the human brain is able to "materialize" mental events through movements. In no other conceivable set of circumstances, as far as is known, do we encounter a similar situation. In the physical movements of man, mind ("going more ghostly than a ghost," as Sherrington wrote) establishes an intimate and demonstrable contact with a kinetic system that forms part of ourselves. Sherrington encompassed the issue by saying that in the energy pattern which is the brain, two sets of events happen which, as far as we know, happen nowhere else in the perceptible universe. As far as our universe is concerned, nowhere in all the immensity of energy does our glimpse detect any relation of energy except to energy save in this one instance, the brain.

If we apply Fernel's imaginative metaphor to the science of sport and physical education we arrive at this conclusion: the measurable characteristics of the phenomena under study represent the "theatre of events"; while those which do not fit into the energy system of physics and mathematics relate to the "events" themselves. To illustrate the first statement, we have the history of athletic performance records seen against the environmental circumstances to which they are related. As regards the second, we shall examine the experiences of individuals who succeeded in attaining superb standards of physical efficiency in the presence of major bodily handicaps, and were thus able to transform their fate.

Since the revival of the Olympic Games in 1896, there has been a steady improvement of all athletic records, for women as well as for men. The rate of this improvement has been fairly constant and there is good reason to predict that it will continue unchanged for a considerable time. The same trends are noticeable in sports as different as weight-lifting and sprinting, swimming and hurdling, long-distance running and polevaulting.

ACCELERATION OF GROWTH

In many parts of the world complex changes in human development have been brought about by the improvements in living conditions which follow technological advances. In countries such as the United States, the Soviet Union and Japan, children now develop more quickly and mature earlier than they did in the past, while adults age more slowly. An 18-year old British high school student of average size could not fit into the mediaeval knight's armour that stands in the Tower of London; the beautiful eighteenth-century wedding dresses on display in the National Museum in Helsinki could not be worn by today's brides in Finland. Between 1879 and now, life expectancy in the United States has more than doubled, from 34 to over 70 years of age. The societies in which these changes are most noticeable produce the greatest number of outstanding athletes.

Socio-economic progress as such does not engender physical fitness; nor does it automatically lead to a reduction in the prevalence of disease. In the United States during the past decade, both President Eisenhower and President Kennedy have drawn attention to an "alarming decline of youth fitness" which they ascribe to the over-abundance of food and lack of physical activity that has accompanied the progressive urbanization and mechanization of life in the United States. Similar trends have been observed in other countries. We are confronted with this interesting paradox: the same societies which produce the greatest numbers of top-class athletes find themselves compelled to adopt measures to counteract a lack of fitness in their youths.

In their book *Hypokinetic Disease,* Professors William Raab and Hans Kraus have shown that, in populations which are physically inactive, there is a steady increase in the incidence of the so-called degenerative diseases, more particularly of the cardiovascular system. During the past fifty years the gradual elemination of infectious diseases has considerably lengthened the span of life, but the relative frequency of degenerative diseases has almost doubled.

NUTRITION AND HEALTH

Professor Ancel Keys' global nutrition survey shows that in societies where degenerative cardiovascular diseases are most

widespread, diets with a conspicuously high caloric, fat and protein content are usually associated with a lack of exercise. Other
data show that physical activity and balanced diets of low fat
and protein content counteract the development of degenerative
changes in the circulatory system.

The exercise factor is very significant in the causation of degenerative diseases. Surveys have shown that people who lead
sedentary lives tend to become fat and are very susceptible to
these degenerative troubles. On the other hand, physically active
people can eat virtually whatever they like without running the
same risks. Professor John Yudkin has demonstrated a close
parallel between rising rates of coronary deaths and the number
of radio and television licenses issued during the past three
decades; this further suggests that the increasing incidence of
cardiovascular diseases is connected with physical inactivity.
Professor J. N. Morris reported that London bus-drivers, who are
compelled to lead an extremely inactive life, are fatter than the
more active bus-conductors, and are more prone to heart disease,
and in a survey conducted during 1960, Dr. Mary Bramwell
demonstrated that this discrepancy between the two groups was
in no way related to the food they ate.[1]

EXERCISE AND LONGEVITY

Professor Karvonen found that the physique and cardiac status
of middle-aged lumberjacks were distinctly superior to those of
sedentary subjects. On the other hand, I recently presented
evidence to the effect that the hearts of former Olympic competitors who had not been in training for ten or more years were
in no way better than those of men of the same age who had
never in their lives taken part in athletics. Finnish skiers live

---

[1] While in many countries both drivers and conductors are seated, the conductors
in the London double-decker buses move about freely to collect their fares, climb up
and down the narrow staircase between the lower and upper deck, and alight at stops.
The significance of Morris's study is due in the first place to his realization of the
opportunity thus offered for an analysis of the long-term implications of the exercise
factor.

eight years longer than their physically inactive compatriots; but in England Sir Alan Rook found no increased life expectancy among those competitors in the Oxford and Cambridge boat race who, after leaving the university, had led inactive lives. In order to be fully beneficial, training must be continued throughout life.

Socio-economic environment and physical training are the two most powerful "external" determinants of health and fitness. Quantitative methods of research, especially the use of statistics, have yielded a great deal of information about the physiological mechanisms upon which human efficiency depends, or in Fernel's words, the "theatre of events."

What about the "events" themselves? In the search for values and for the meaning of sport and athletics, all the biochemical, statistical and mechanical analyses and assessments of human movement provide no final criteria. Structures and measurements do not possess a soul. The motor acts involved in sport and physical education are themselves the "events," played on a stage whose material presence merely provides a time and place for their occurrence.

MOTIVATION AND EXPERIENCE

Great advances in our knowledge of the human aspects of motor events have resulted from the efforts of a group of distinguished physicans and philosophers led by Professors Erwin Straus in the United States, Merleau Ponty in France, Ludwig Binswanger in Switzerland, F. J. J. Buytendijk in Holland and Jurg Zutt in Germany. These scientists have introduced an approach to the study of motor behaviour which helps us to understand how physical movements take place and also how certain intangibles which accompany them, such as motivation and experience affect their performance. The scope of this new approach can best be illustrated by the stories of three remarkable individuals who reached the summit of athletic prowess in spite of major physical handicaps. By developing their motor resources, these people not only attained exceptional performance levels, but in doing so they also altered the meaning of their human existence which had seemed to be immutably fixed.

THREE CHAMPIONS

Harold Connolly, the greatest hammer-thrower of his time and winner of the Olympic gold medal in 1956, has a severely crippled left arm caused by a combined injury of both upper and lower brachial plexuses due to a birth trauma. The condition caused a marked growth defect as well as generalized pareses and paralyses of the muscles of the arm on the affected side.

Karoly Takacs of Hungary ranks as one of the best marksmen (pistol shooting) in the world. When, as a young student, he participated in the Olympic Games in 1936, he was already known as an outstanding performer. In 1938, he was involved in an accident which necessitated amputation of the right arm midway between elbow and wrist; he subsequently competed holding his pistol in the left hand. In 1939 he won a world championship. At the Olympic Games in London in 1948 and in Helsinki in 1952 he was awarded gold medals. The 1956 Games in Australia were his fourth Olympic competition.

Lis Hartel of Denmark was declared the world's leading equestrienne at the dressage competitions of the Olympic Games in Helsinki in 1952 and in Stockholm in 1956. Since her school days, Mrs. Hartel had been a good rider. At the age of 23, seven years before her first Olympic contest, she suffered an attack of poliomyelitis which caused major irremediable paralyses of all four extremities, whose mobility and strength were reduced by more than 50 per cent. At Helsinki she still had to use leg braces and crutches for standing and walking. The nature and extent of the physical handicaps caused by the above-mentioned conditions have been described in many textbooks of neurology and orthopaedic surgery, all of which take it for granted that patients thus afflicted are permanently disabled. Because of the irremediable nature of their handicaps the three athletes seemed to belong to the category of "the lame and the halt" of whom the Bible speaks with compassion; to a class of human beings who throughout history have been looked upon as *les misérables,* to whom no alternative was left but to accept their destiny with resignation. The significance of these case histories lies in the fact that they demonstrate once and for all the fallacy of this attitude. Confronted with physical defects of considerable magnitude, the three champions changed their destiny by making defiant and heroic decisions of their own. Prometheus-like, they challenged fate itself.

The performance techniques which these three athletes learned to master did not rest upon reflex-controlled muscular patterns like those of standing, walking and running, which are inborn. On the contrary, these Olympic champions excelled in muscular activities that had to be synthesized from distinct mental images, in order to achieve clearly conceived objectives. Attempting any of these activities required powerful motivation and sustained perseverance of effort; for their execution, original nerve-muscle combinations had to be invented, as alternatives to the normal nerve-muscle combinations rendered unserviceable by their handicaps.

THE WISDOM OF THE BODY

In the early 1920s, the British physiologist Ernest Starling introduced the idea of a "wisdom of the body" which had suggested itself to him while reading, in the Book of Job, "Who hath put wisdom in the inward parts? Or who hath given understanding to the heart?"[1]

Starling was impressed by what appeared to him to be a quality of purposiveness in the responses of the heart to stimuli which he applied in his experiments with animals. He asked himself whether, as a general principle in nature, all biological adaptations possess an intrinsic quality of wisdom. Similar questions had been raised earlier by pathologists who attempted to give a wider interpretation to certain bodily reactions to injury, e.g., formation of scar and callous tissue in the repair of damage to skin and bone. Some investigators had maintained that these adjustments provided definite evidence of a *vis medicatrix naturae* (power of natural healing).

Does such a *vis medicatrix naturae* exist? As far back as 1872, Julius Cohnheim in Breslau undertook a critical examination of the question. He presented a great deal of evidence in support of his view that we have no reason to suppose the animal body to be endowed with properties that are designed to meet patho-

---

[1] Job xxxviii, 36.

logical emergencies, even though it certainly does so at times. Cohnheim showed that many reactions to disease or injury are associated with such disorder and failure that it is impossible to detect the principle of adaptation.

However, our Olympic champions' responses to the challenge of their handicaps were not "directed" by impersonal biological forces. On the contrary, they revealed individual judgement, courage and intelligence, attributes which cannot be measured by the "exact natural sciences."

To return to Professor Medawar's concept of the two systems of heredity, the endosomatic based upon predetermined interplay of chromosomes, and the exosomatic, passed down through culture and tradition: sport and physical education belong, in the last resort, to the second system, because they are a product of the human mind. *The story of sport and physical education exemplifies the wisdom of man imposing his influence upon the wisdom of nature.* With the spread of physical education, human thinking and human ingenuity have created a dynamic force that has modified the state of existence of entire societies by extending their freedom of action.

Sport and physical education thus fall within a humanistic concept, according to which all affairs of men originate in the minds of men, and the unique contribution which they are destined to make to the welfare of society must be conceived and formulated step by step on the intellectual level. It is in this context that Unesco's support of the International Council of Sport and Physical Education assumes its real significance.

AUTHOR INDEX

SUBJECT INDEX